Dreaming o

D0447511

T.A. WILLIAMS
Dreaming of Christmas

CANELO

First published in the United Kingdom in 2018 by Canelo

This edition published in the United Kingdom in 2020 by

Canelo Digital Publishing Limited
31 Helen Road
Oxford OX2 0DF
United Kingdom

A CIP catalogue record for this book is available from the British Library.

Print ISBN 978 1 78863 976 7
Ebook ISBN 978 1 78863 095 5

Look for more great books at www.canelo.co

Printed and bound in Great Britain by Clays Ltd, Elcograf S.p.A.

To Mariangela and Christina with love, as always

Prologue

'Zoë, we need to talk.'

'What about?' Zoë was making notes and didn't raise her eyes from the recipe book open in front of her.

'About us.'

'What about us? I've got to stuff the turkey and start getting the veg ready. In case you'd forgotten, it's Christmas Day tomorrow and we've got my parents coming. What's the matter? Has something happened?'

'Yes, something's happened.'

There was something about Grant's tone that made her look up. Directly behind his head, the Christmas decorations had slipped off the corner of the kitchen cupboard, but she was far too busy to think about fiddling with tinsel and mistletoe this morning.

'What is it?'

She saw him take a deep breath. 'It's like this, Zoë. I've found somebody else.'

She sat bolt upright, not trusting her ears.

'You've what?'

He was wearing his sheepish expression, the one normally reserved for those times when he came home hours later than promised, reeking of beer, after an evening with his rugby-playing mates.

'I've found somebody else, Zo. I'm leaving.'

'Leaving? You mean leaving me... this flat?' For an intelligent woman, her brain function was remarkably slow this morning.

She saw him nod his head. The sheepish expression had now been replaced by his equally familiar stubborn look.

'Things haven't been so great between us for a while now, have they?'

'They haven't?'

As she asked the question, her brain slowly started working again. Maybe he was right. It wasn't as if they had been arguing any more than usual, but on reflection, they hadn't been talking much either. Her job in particular had been taking up more and more of her free time, and he had been away a lot. Maybe he had a point. She started to formulate a reply, but he carried on.

'I haven't been happy for quite some time now, and I just can't go on as we are.'

'But you haven't said anything... and now, all of a sudden...?'

'Would it have made any difference? Let's face it, you're more interested in your job than you are in me.'

'That's not fair, Grant. I work hard, but I still care about you. Surely you can see that?'

'Not from where I'm standing. Ten years is a long time, Zo. I think it's time to make a fresh start. My mind's made up. I'll collect my things and leave straight away.'

'You're leaving *now*?' She was genuinely stunned, even to the extent of wondering if this might all be a dream – a very bad dream. 'That's leaving... as in leaving forever?'

'Forever, Zo.' He hesitated for a few moments. 'I'm sorry.'

As Zoë's brain finally kicked into gear, she felt a surge of different emotions burning through her, uppermost of which was anger – coupled with disbelief. She knew he could be thoughtless, but his sense of timing was worse than that. By far.

'And you thought that today, the day before Christmas, would be the best moment to tell me you're leaving after ten years together? Did I get that right?'

He pushed back his chair and stood up, his cornflakes only half-eaten.

'I'm afraid so. Like I say, Zo, I'm sorry.'

'And who is this other woman?'

'Her name's Claire. I know her from kitesurfing.'

It was beginning to sink in properly now. The woman had a name. He meant it. He was leaving.

Hot on the heels of the anger, she could feel something even more powerful building inside her and she knew it was sorrow – a deep, dark, all-consuming sadness that rose and threatened to spread across her like a shroud. Her stomach turned to ice, her knees to jelly, and her eyes began to sting. Rather than let him see her break down and cry like a baby, she turned away, uttering the last words she would say to him in this house.

'Then I suppose you'd better go.'

He made no response, but she heard the door close behind him.

There was so much she didn't understand, so much she hadn't asked, so much he hadn't said. For a moment she almost followed him out of the door to try to get more sense out of him, but she stopped herself. His tone had said it all. He was leaving and that was that.

Chapter 1

The radio in the car said this was the hottest day of the year. At least, that appeared to be the message – the loose connection somewhere under the dashboard meant that Zoë only heard about half of what was said. Even now, at half past six, and with all four windows open, she was sweating buckets as she drove home after spending a few days with her parents in Bath. She didn't need the radio to tell her it was hot.

The lights changed to red as she reached the crossroads just before her turning and she pulled up, fanning herself with this week's copy of *Hello Celebrity* magazine from the pile on the seat beside her. As she sat there quietly melting, she glanced to her left and saw the familiar kitesurfing poster in the travel agent's window, and as always, she thought of Grant. He had been crazy about the sport.

He doubtless still was.

She was helpless to prevent a growl from escaping her lips, and she immediately felt annoyed with herself that he could still get to her. Grant had no place in her thoughts or her life any more and she had been working so hard to forget him. But all it had needed was a casual glimpse of a poster to bring it all back, and she felt a wave of frustration. After the way he had behaved, she had considerable sympathy with those women you read about who chopped up all their exes' clothes and dumped them on the pavement. But along with anger, there was still the ever-present cold sense of loss she had been feeling since Christmas. She had loved him, but she had lost him – or rather, he had turned his back on her.

The lights changed and she drove the last half-mile to her flat, gradually calming her still raw emotions. She was a little bit later than normal and all the parking spaces in front had already been taken, so she had to park round the corner in the spot where vehicles regularly got vandalised. As she locked the car and checked that she had left nothing of value inside, she reflected that the only good thing about not having a better car was the fact that this one looked as if it had already been vandalised. Hopefully that would make it a less attractive target for the mindless adolescents round here.

She had barely stepped into her flat when the phone started ringing. Pushing the door closed behind her, she set down her weekend bag and her briefcase and answered it.

'Zoë Lumsley, hello.'

'Hi, Zo, it's me.'

'Hi, Jules. Long time no speak. How're things with you?'

She and Juliet had shared a tacky old house with a bunch of other students when they were in their last year at university. That was all of ten years ago now and she had pretty much lost contact with most of the others – apart from Grant, of course. She and Juliet had remained really good friends and, seeing as they both lived in London, normally managed to meet up several times a year, but she realised she hadn't heard from her since the winter, and now it was already late summer.

'Not bad really. I've moved on from A&E and have suddenly discovered my life again. I even find I have the time and energy to go out in the evenings.'

While Zoë had studied English, Juliet had studied medicine and had plunged straight from university into the busiest period in the history of the health service. Zoë was really pleased to hear her sounding cheery for a change. The last time they had met up – shortly after Grant had left – the evening they had spent together had been more like a funerary wake.

'Brilliant news. You deserve a bit of time off.'

'And how about you, Zo, and Grant…?'

There was no need for her to say more. Immediately after Zoë and Grant had split up last Christmas, Juliet's had been one of the first numbers Zoë had called, knowing she could count on her friend for support and advice. As a result, Juliet knew all the gory details of how the ten-year relationship had gone down the plughole so swiftly. And so unexpectedly, at least as far as Zoë was concerned.

Zoë answered as determinedly as she could. 'I'm fine. I don't know if you heard I'd changed jobs. The new one's not exactly my dream job, but it'll tide me over until I find something better. And as for Grant, I'll survive.' She was pleased to hear her voice sounding fairly firm. She now managed to talk about her ex without welling up or boiling over, but it had taken time. A long time.

'So, no replacement lined up?'

'For Grant? God, no. I have no intention of getting involved with another man, thank you very much.'

'What, never?'

7

Over the past few weeks, Zoë had begun to ask herself the same question. Eight months had gone by and she was gradually starting to think about Grant less and less. Pretty soon now the time would come for her to begin to get on with her life once more, but maybe not quite yet. She attempted an honest answer.

'Well, maybe not never, but for now, I'm happy enough as I am. I'm not exactly being paid a fortune, but I can afford the rent, and the job certainly keeps me busy.'

'So what's the new job? Still journalism, I presume.'

'*Hello Celebrity* magazine. You can probably work out its *raison d'être* for yourself. The clue's in the title.'

'Writing about the lives of the rich and famous?'

'Would-be rich and would-be famous, mostly, but yes. *HC* magazine may not be *The Times*, but it sells, unlike most newspapers these days.'

Her previous job with a big national daily paper had suddenly finished back at Easter when the owners had announced they were having to restructure. After almost eight years with them, she had found herself out of a job. Coming on top of Grant's desertion, it had added to making this a really tough year – what Ron the photographer had described with his usual gutter humour as her *'anus' horribilis*. As an English graduate, the spelling annoyed her, but she couldn't fault the sentiment. It had been brutal.

'But like I say, Jules, it's keeping me busy while I look for something a bit more to my taste. I find myself working all hours, and my boss is one of those workaholics who expects the rest of us to have no personal life as well. Luckily for me, I have no personal life these days, so I fit in fine.' Realising that this sounded a bit too gloomy, she hastily injected a bit more cheer into her tone. 'But for now, it's okay. Being so busy means I don't really have the time for a man – even if I was in the market for one, which I'm not.'

She sensed scepticism at the other end of the line, but then, mercifully, Juliet changed the subject.

'Anyway, Zo, apart from seeing how you are, the other reason I was calling was to ask if you'd got Billy's invitation.'

'Invitation? To be honest, I've just come back from a few days with Mum and I've got a pile of post here I haven't looked at yet. Billy, did you say? Computer Billy?'

Computer Billy had been Grant's nickname for their nerdy friend who had occupied the little attic room on the top floor of their student house. She hadn't seen or heard from him for years now.

'Yes, and it sounds amazing.' Juliet paused. 'I tell you what. You check out the invite and then call me back. See what you think. If you're going, I'll go.'

Zoë dropped the phone and picked up the half-dozen envelopes lying on her doormat. She sifted through the bills and flyers until she found the one she was looking for. It bore an Austrian stamp and it had been typewritten. She slit it open with her fingernail and pulled out a handsome printed card. There was a company name and address at the top and the invitation read:

Mr William Fischer

requests the pleasure of your company at

the Grand Hotel Schlossberg,
Bad Bergstein, Austria

From 18th to 27th December

Her name had been written in the top right-hand corner, and she immediately recognised the spidery handwriting as Billy's. He had added *PTO* at the bottom and, turning the card over, she saw he had scrawled a message.

> *Hi Zoë,*
>
> *Hope you're well. I'm organising a little reunion for those of us who lived at number 23. It's been ten years now and I thought it would be fun to meet up and compare notes. I do so hope you can come. I'm dying to see you again after so long.*
> *Billy*
> *PS My treat.*

My treat? Zoë had heard that Billy had done pretty well for himself since leaving university, but treating all the people who had shared the house with him to a holiday in an Austrian hotel was going to cost a packet – especially over the Christmas period. Her eyes flicked back to the address at the top of the card. The name of the company was WF Computer Systems, and she remembered he had set up his own business shortly after leaving university.

She retrieved her laptop from her briefcase and did a quick search. It very soon emerged that WF Computer Systems had grown exponentially over the last ten years and was now internationally acclaimed, as was its founder and CEO, the reclusive William Fischer, aka Computer Billy. The address in the historic city of Salzburg was described as the company's European centre of operations. A hasty scan down the Wikipedia entry revealed that Billy's rise to superstardom in the world of electronics had been meteoric. From penniless nerd ten years ago, his company had emerged as a major international player, with hundreds, maybe thousands, of employees around the globe.

Zoë exhaled in amazement. Good old Billy. She spotted a sheet of paper left in the envelope and pulled it out. It was headed *Information* and it detailed what Billy's treat was to be. Bad Bergstein, it transpired, was a ski resort and thermal spa to the south of Salzburg in Austria, and he was offering full board and lodging there for a week before Christmas and a couple of days after. They would be accommodated in deluxe single or double rooms (*please specify*), provided with ski and boot hire (*if required*), skiing lessons (*if required*) and a ski pass for the duration (*if required*). The hotel had a swimming pool and thermal baths – the *Bad* in Bad Bergstein meant 'bath' – as well as a fitness centre at the disposal of the guests. Transfers would be provided from Salzburg airport and back (*please give flight information*) and there would be a gala ball on Christmas Eve (*dress code: smart*). It all sounded wonderful.

Zoë picked up her phone and called Juliet back.

'Wow, Jules, I heard Billy was doing well, but… wow!' The more she thought about it, the more amazing it sounded.

'I know, right? He says it'll be his treat, but it's going to cost the earth. Have you checked out the hotel?'

'No, but I imagine it's pretty swanky.'

'Pretty swanky? Zoë, have you got a computer there? Just google it. Go on. I'll wait.'

Zoë did as she was told and her amazement grew.

The Grand Hotel Schlossberg was a luxury hotel built in the traditional Tyrolean style, five or six storeys tall, with white walls and carved wooden balustrades to the balconies. In the summer these balustrades were hung with window boxes overflowing with red and white flowers, and the winter shots showed the surrounding fir trees laden with snow. The very top floor, under the eaves, was clad with dark timber, and a thick layer of snow on the gently sloping roof gave it a very cosy air. According to the blurb, it was possible to ski from there to the ski lifts and directly back to the hotel again. Pictures of the interior were every bit as impressive as the facade, and Zoë had to agree with Juliet's judgement – yes, it certainly looked swanky.

'Blimey, Jules, what a place. It looks incredible. Talk about luxury! So, are you up for it? Can you get the time off?'

'As just about the only unmarried surgeon in the hospital, I've worked right through the last three Christmases, so they owe me. Yes, I'm definitely up for it – as long as you are.' Zoë heard her hesitate. 'But Zo, you realise what this means? If he's inviting all of us, then that'll mean Grant as well.'

Zoë suddenly had a very rude awakening. She had been so caught up in the excitement of imagining herself in the mountains, she had forgotten about her ex. She and Grant had hooked up during their final year at university and had lived at number 23 as a couple alongside the others. If Billy was inviting everybody from the house, he would no doubt also invite Grant. In fact, there was no reason for him to assume that she and Grant weren't still together. Although she had lost contact with Billy over the past few years, the last time they had been in touch, she and Grant had still been an item.

She took a deep breath.

'Bugger! For a moment there, I wasn't thinking.'

'He might not come, though, Zo.'

'He'll come all right. Anything to get out on the ski slopes. Besides, the place looks phenomenal.'

'But even if he says yes, you're still going to come, aren't you?' There was a pleading note to Juliet's voice.

Zoë stopped to consider her options, but memories of her time with Grant came sweeping back once more, unbidden. The only contact she had had with him since last Christmas had been occasional emails about everyday things like bills, or the deposit on the flat, and she hadn't met up with him at all. She felt the blood rush to her cheeks and the familiar stinging in the corners of her eyes that she thought she had outgrown. Along with this came a surge of the anger that his callous departure had aroused, which still bubbled beneath the surface. The idea of seeing him again made her blood boil and her heart sink at the same time.

'I really don't think I can, Jules. I'm sorry. It's all too fresh. I'd only make myself miserable, or I might end up trying to push him off a balcony or something. Either way, I'd ruin it for everybody else.'

'Of course you wouldn't. You've got to get on with your life, Zo. He behaved like a heartless moron, but you're bigger than that.' Juliet's voice was low and her tone supportive. 'Anyway, I've got an idea. What're you doing tomorrow night?'

'Um… nothing special.'

'How about meeting up for a drink? I finish work at six. It's only half an hour on the train down to you. I could be there for seven. That way you can sleep on it first. Promise me you won't make any hasty decisions.'

'All right, I promise.'

Although deep down inside, the idea of seeing Grant again filled her with dread.

Chapter 2

Next day at work, Zoë was too busy to spend much time thinking about the invitation to Austria, but she had done more than enough worrying overnight. In fact, although she had finally drifted off to sleep in the small hours, she had tossed and turned for ages first. Of course Juliet was right. It was time she got on with the rest of her life, but the idea of not only seeing Grant again but being cooped up with him in a hotel for a week was both intimidating and infuriating.

His announcement last Christmas that he had found another woman and was leaving had come as a bolt from the blue – or as near as made no difference. Yes, there had probably been a few little doubts in her mind, but nothing she could put her finger on. Considering she was a journalist, it rankled with her that she had been so blind to what was going on. Of course, she had been aware that her workload meant she had been seeing less and less of him over the last few years of their relationship. And his business trips away – often involving weekends as well – had been getting more frequent, but she had never seriously thought he might have somebody else. The tragic fact of the matter was that she had loved him in spite of everything, and losing him really had broken her heart. Beneath the anger she still felt towards him was bitter grief. How would she feel about seeing him again?

Then, sometime in the small hours, she had suddenly sat bolt upright in bed, eyes wide open, at the thought that he would almost certainly turn up in Austria with his new woman. The idea of meeting her was immensely unpalatable. With that thought lodged in her mind, it had been a long night.

Consequently, she wasn't feeling at her chirpiest the next morning as she shared a taxi with Ron the photographer en route to an interview with a B-list movie actor hungry for publicity. Her lack of enthusiasm, however, was more than compensated for by her companion. Ron was positively bouncy.

'Like the new jacket, sweetheart?'

She hadn't noticed. She turned her head and took a look. It was a brown leather bomber jacket and it looked pretty good on him. He wasn't a bad-looking man, as long as you didn't concentrate too much on what he was like underneath the skin. As far as she was concerned, Ron was an acquired taste – rather like creosote or silage. She nodded her head and told him what he wanted to hear.

'Very nice. Expensive?'

'Five hundred quid.'

'Blimey, Ron, did you win the lottery?'

He shook his head. 'No, I'm doing a bit of work on the side. And it pays well.'

'Wedding photography?'

'No, very different. Here, take a look.'

He pulled out his phone and scrolled through a whole heap of photos until he found the one he wanted.

'What do you think of that, sweetheart? Good, eh?'

Zoë took the phone from him and squinted at it. With the taxi weaving in and out of the traffic in the streets of east London, it wasn't easy. She held the phone closer to her eyes. It took a few more seconds before she suddenly realised what she was looking at.

'For God's sake, Ron, that's disgusting.'

She almost threw the phone back at him and rubbed her hands on her coat in an attempt to remove the contagion. He looked not only unapologetic but positively buoyed, by her comment. There was a broad lascivious grin on his face.

'These folk pay me well, and they pay the girls well too. If you ever want to supplement your wages, just say the word. With your face and figure, I'm sure it could be a nice little earner for you.'

'Oh God…'

–

The actor – whose name was Dan Greenfinch – had come across the Atlantic to London to co-star in a low-budget movie about zombies invading Canary Wharf. His face looked seriously weathered, and when Zoë and Ron were shown into his trailer to interview him, her first impression was that he had maybe already applied zombie make-up. It subsequently transpired that he hadn't and Zoë didn't envy the make-up artists if he had to appear in a non-zombie role. The actor – 'Call me Dan' – did his best to be hospitable by asking her if she wanted a 'line'. This was not the first interview she had done with showbiz folk, and she now knew what was intended by this invitation, so she hastily shook her head.

'Thanks, I'm working.'

'Mind if I do?'

'No, go ahead.'

She then had to sit there while Call-me-Dan snorted a line of cocaine up his nose. It wasn't a pretty sight. Subsequently, as he answered her questions, he spent most of his time rubbing his nose, snuffling and sneezing. She shuddered surreptitiously.

The interview took about half an hour, and then Ron spent another half-hour taking a load of photos of the actor. Once she had finished and Ron had gone off with the PR girl to take some shots of the set, Call-me-Dan indicated that he rather liked the look of Zoë. As she was shaking hands with him, he gave her a lecherous leer and informed her that sex with him would undoubtedly be the high point of her life to date. For once, Zoë was grateful to Ron. This was the fifth time in four months that she had been propositioned by celebrities, and the photographer had been happy to provide her with a very effective way of refusing, without fear of being bothered any further. Keeping a straight face, she told Call-me-Dan she regretted she would not be able to accept his kind offer.

'I'm afraid I haven't had the all-clear from the doctor yet.'

She didn't say any more, but comprehension dawned on the pockmarked face in front of her, and she was able to leave unmolested. Unless she counted the sensation of disgust she carried with her all the way back in the taxi.

She spent the next couple of hours writing a two-thousand-word piece entitled 'Zombies vs Canaries'. Just after lunch, she sent it through to Damien, the editor, and waited for his verdict. She didn't have to wait long. The phone on her desk buzzed almost immediately, and he was as succinct as ever.

'Zoë. Get in here. Now.'

She made her way along the corridor to his office, knocked, and went in without waiting for an answer.

'You wanted to see me, Damien?'

As usual, he was sitting with his back to the window so as to dazzle and intimidate anyone who came to sit opposite him. He was wearing his usual blue striped shirt with a white collar and cuffs, the collar open and the sleeves rolled up. He wore the same thing every day, and opinion in the office fell into two camps. There were those who believed he had a stock of the shirts, one for every day of the week, while others – amongst them Zoë – felt sure he had just the one and never took it off.

'Yes, Zoë. Come in. Sit down.' She did as instructed and he immediately launched into a critique of her piece. The crux of the problem could be summarised as 'You didn't like the guy, did you?'

'Not in the slightest. He was a slimy piece of pond life, and if the next time I see him is on my deathbed, it'll be too soon.'

'Listen, Zoë, nobody says you've got to like these people. *I* don't like many of them, but that's not the point. His film company has just paid for six full-page adverts in *HC* magazine and two of our subsidiaries. That pays the bills, and that includes your salary. While I admire your prose, describing him as having "the personality and complexion of a fly cemetery biscuit" is not only insulting, it's probably actionable. So go back over it, tone it down, and for God's sake try to *sound* as if you like him. All right? Got that?'

Zoë spent the rest of the afternoon doing as she had been instructed. At the end of the day, before going off to meet Juliet, she emailed the piece to Damien with one line: *Sanitised for your convenience. Zoë.*

–

As she sat at a table outside by the river that evening, waiting for Juliet to appear, Zoë sipped her Prosecco and turned the conundrum of Billy's invitation round and round in her head. On the one hand, the idea of seeing her ex again was challenging, but at the same time, the thought of a week in a luxury hotel on the ski slopes had considerable appeal. She was still no nearer a conclusion when she felt a tap on her shoulder. She looked up and smiled.

'Jules, hi. Wow, you look great.'

'From the surprise in your voice, I assume I looked like crap last time you saw me.' Juliet was smiling back at her.

Zoë jumped to her feet and they hugged warmly.

'Not crap, but weary. Mind you, only a few days after Grant's bombshell, I don't suppose I looked too brilliant.' She waved Juliet into a seat. 'I got a bottle of Prosecco. Will that do?'

'It'll do perfectly. You know me so well, Zo.'

They both sat down, and Zoë removed the bottle from the cooler and filled their glasses, secretly rather proud that she managed to do it without mishap. She had a bit of a reputation for spilling stuff. As she set the bottle back in the cooler, she looked across at Juliet and raised her glass.

'Cheers, Jules, and I'm delighted to hear your new job's working out.'

'It's a breath of fresh air after the relentless pressure of A&E. Most of the patients I see these days are anaesthetised, and none of them are roaring drunk. But you're looking a good deal better too, Zo. It's been a tough year for you, but it looks as though you're getting over it now.'

Zoë made no reply as she pushed Juliet's glass across the table to her. This was mainly because she didn't really know what state she was in or what to say about it. Instead, they talked about their lives over the months since they had last met, and Zoë gradually let herself be persuaded into agreeing that things were maybe looking up – a bit. After a while, Juliet turned the conversation round to Billy's invitation.

'So, what about Christmas? I presume you've had time to think things through.'

Zoë nodded. 'I've certainly done a lot of thinking, but I'm not much closer to making a decision.'

'But you haven't definitely dismissed the idea – that's good. Listen, I've been thinking too, and here's the way I see it. Grant behaved like a total arse last Christmas and he broke your heart, but there's no need for him to screw up your whole life. He left and that's that. You need to move on and show him you have a life without him. You need something to dream about. Start dreaming of Christmas – next Christmas, not last Christmas. This offer of an all-expenses-paid holiday is exactly what you need. After all, you love skiing, don't you?'

Zoë nodded. She and Grant had taken a year out after university to run a chalet in the French Alps, and both of them had emerged as keen and proficient skiers as a result. Or, to be precise, she had emerged a skier and he a snowboarder.

'I know, Jules, but it's the thought of seeing him again…'

'You're not going to tell me you still have feelings for him? Not after what he did to you.'

'No… Oh, I don't know. I loved him dearly. I really thought he was The One. I suppose there's a part of me somewhere that still thinks of him like that.'

'Like the poor little dog that's been whipped but still comes back to its master?'

'When you put it like that, I know it sounds lame, but I just don't know how I feel. Besides, he'll no doubt turn up with his new woman, and I'm quite sure I don't want to have anything to do with her.'

They talked on and on as the sun dropped lower in the sky, turning the waters of the Thames blood red. Gradually, prompted by Juliet, Zoë began to come round to believing that her friend was right. It took a couple of hours, but eventually, she managed to make up her mind.

'You're right, Jules.' She took a deep breath. 'Why should I turn down the chance of a week's skiing in the lap of luxury just because my ex is going to be there? Enough time's passed. I need to put Grant behind me and move on, don't I? I think I can manage to be civil for a week, and if he can't, then we just won't speak.'

She eyed the now empty wine bottle and wondered to what extent it had contributed to this decision. Would she regret it in the morning?

'Great.' Juliet sounded relieved. 'And don't forget, I'm going to be there on my own as well, so we can stick together. So that's a yes, then?'

Zoë took a deep breath. 'All right, yes, Jules, I'm up for it. It'll be good to see Billy and the others after so long. I'll email my acceptance as soon as I get home tonight.'

'Terrific. I'll do the same.' Juliet held out her glass and clinked it against Zoë's again. 'Cheers! Here's to a week – more than a week – in the lap of luxury. By the way, you realise this means we're going to need something smart for the Christmas Eve ball?'

'Cheers, Jules, and thanks for bullying me into it. And yes, I suppose I'd better think about going dress shopping. I've hardly bought a thing this year. Why don't you and I meet up in town when the pre-Christmas sales start, and go shopping together?'

'Great idea. I wonder if the others will all dress up.'

'I'm sure they will – especially Imogen.'

'Have you heard anything from her? I haven't heard a word since uni.'

'Not a sausage. Mind you, we did have a fairly major falling-out right before we all left, didn't we?'

Imogen had not been the easiest of people to share a house with. Apart from her obsessive occupation of the bathroom and her ability to drain all the hot water in the house at one sitting, the main problem had been that she was a fully committed social climber – one of those people who are never satisfied with their lot. Allegedly from a very well-heeled family – although nobody had ever seen or heard from them – she had managed to get on everybody's nerves. Even normally pacific Juliet had come close to emptying the remains of a can of stale beer over her head after one of her more outrageous utterances.

'I think I heard somewhere that she'd got married a few years back, but I'm not sure.'

'Well, maybe this means we'll get to see the husband. I bet he's filthy rich. Mind you, I suppose she might decide not to come.'

'And miss an all-expenses-paid holiday in a luxury hotel?'

Zoë nodded to herself. The other thing about Imogen had been her allergy to spending money. Juliet was right. If it was free, Imogen would be up for it.

'Ah well, we'll see. It's been almost ten years. Maybe she's mellowed.'

'You think?'

Juliet didn't sound too convinced, but after a pause, she smiled across at Zoë.

'Mandy and Martin's little girl must be, what, five now? It's still funny to think of them with a child. And it'll be fun to meet up with Lorna again. Her bedpost must have so many notches in it by now, it's probably about to collapse under the strain.'

Zoë giggled at the thought. Certainly Lorna's bed at number 23 had been well used, and they had all grown very familiar – and fed up – with the grunts and groans emanating from there on a regular basis. Zoë had lost count of the number of men she had seen emerging from Lorna's bedroom in the grey light of dawn, looking as if they had just done ten rounds with a prizefighter.

'I wonder if she's got herself a serious partner now, or if she's still playing the field.'

'No doubt we'll get to hear all about it. I did hear that she's got a new job – sounds like a big step up – so maybe she's like you and losing herself in her work. Anyway, Zo, I can't wait. So for the next few months, we can both start dreaming of Christmas. Next Christmas, remember, not last. Right?'

'Right.'

Under the table, Zoë's fingers were firmly crossed.

Chapter 3

It was one day in early November that Zoë made a big mistake.

She was chatting at the coffee machine with Rudolph, from the lifestyle and fashion desk – generally known around the office as Rudolph the Brown-Nosed Reindeer for his habit of cosying up to his superiors. In a moment of distraction, she happened to mention where she was going for Christmas. Later that afternoon, she was summoned to Damien's office. Suspiciously, he was smiling. This was always something of a rarity, and it normally didn't bode well.

'So, Zoë, I gather you're going skiing this Christmas.'

'Yes, Damien, that's right.'

She gave herself a mental kicking, but it was too late now. The cat was out of the bag.

'And it's all courtesy of an old friend of yours from your student days?'

'Erm, yes.'

'One William Fischer, I believe?' He didn't wait for her reply. 'Or to apply the epithet bestowed upon him by the world's media, the *reclusive* founder of WF Computers. Right?'

'If you say so, Damien.'

'I do say so, Zoë. Well, I've been doing a bit of thinking. You've been here for almost six months now, and we're very pleased with the way you're working out. It would be nice to see you in a more responsible position – naturally with a pay rise and a few perks, maybe a car. You'd like that, wouldn't you?'

Zoë nodded her head even more cautiously, beginning to realise where this was leading.

'Now, given that you're an old friend of the reclusive Mr Fischer, I was thinking how good it would be if you could get *HC* magazine an exclusive about the man, his company, his home, his wardrobe, his personal life, his wife, girlfriend or boyfriend. You know, a full exposé for our readers. If you can get some photos, even better, although I'd be prepared to send over a photographer if necessary.' His smile broadened – or it might have been acid indigestion. 'Now, how do you feel about that as an idea?'

Zoë knew when she was trapped. If she refused, she had few illusions as to her future here at *HC*. Although she had been keeping an eye on the jobs websites, journalism was in crisis at the moment, with papers all round the country closing down as people increasingly got their news from their phones. She really needed to hang onto the *HC* job at least until she found something better. Regretfully she nodded, but did her best to insert a few caveats in her acceptance.

'I'll do my best, Damien, but I wouldn't want to do anything to screw up my friendship with Billy... William.'

'Of course, of course.' The bonhomie Damien was exuding was disturbing.

'I'll certainly try to put something together, but I can't betray his hospitality or his trust. You do understand that, don't you, Damien?'

'Naturally, Zoë. I'm sure you'll be able to square the circle. Excellent.'

As the weeks passed, she still found herself dreaming of Christmas, but now she had two things to worry her: not only being reunited with Grant and meeting his new woman, but also having in effect to spy on her old friend. Both were uncomfortable prospects.

—

In early December, she met up with Juliet in central London, their mission to find themselves suitably smart gowns for the Christmas Eve gala ball. Zoë was delighted to see Juliet again and to see her looking so good. She was definitely sounding much happier since moving from A&E, although there might, of course, be another reason for the transformation. The journalist in Zoë couldn't resist doing a bit of digging as they sat in the cafe on the top floor of John Lewis in Oxford Street.

'The big smile on your face, Jules – could it be down to something other than your job? Maybe somebody special?'

She saw Juliet's cheeks flush and wondered if she had struck gold, but the answer did little to clarify the situation.

'Nobody special, Zo. But now I've finally got a bit of time to myself, I've definitely been making some new friends. I've bought myself a bike and I go cycling most weekends with a bunch of people. Most of them are nice – some very nice.'

'Male and female?'

Juliet gave her a long-suffering look. 'Yes, Zoë, men *and* women, but I'm not about to leap into a deep and meaningful relationship any time soon, if that's what you're hinting at. Friends, Zo, just friends.' She caught Zoë's eye across the table. 'Besides, after your experience of deep and meaningful relationships, I would have thought you'd be the last person to be pushing me into one.'

Zoë nodded apologetically. 'Sorry, Jules. Just natural curiosity. You're bright and you're good-looking, I'd have thought you'd be hitched by now, that's all.'

'It'll happen for both of us in due course, if we want it to. After all, we're both only just thirty-two. There's bags of time.'

'Yes, I know, and you're right.'

She took a sip of her cappuccino and looked around the store, realising how little she had been out this year. It really did feel good to be doing something other than working or sitting in her flat on her own.

'It's taken me the best part of a year, but it's only just now that I'm beginning to realise that there *is* life beyond Grant. After acting as his personal housekeeper for years while he went gallivanting around all over the place, I've been starting to think I should maybe look around for some new friends of my own.'

'That sounds much better than the last time we talked. I was afraid for a while that you still hadn't got over everything that happened.'

Zoë shook her head. 'It's been a long, hard slog, but I think I'm just about there.'

'So the thought of seeing him again in a few weeks' time doesn't bother you any more?'

'Of course it bothers me, Jules. I really have no idea how I'm going to react – or how *he'll* react for that matter. But I'm going to tough it out. I need to.'

'Good for you, Zo. And just keep reminding yourself how badly he hurt you. He's always been a smooth talker. Don't let him persuade you into doing something you know you'll regret.'

'Oh, I won't forget how he treated me, Jules. Believe me.'

They spent a couple of hours and quite a bit of money kitting themselves out for the ball, and Zoë couldn't suppress a feeling of growing excitement at the prospect of spending a week in the mountains – and in a luxury hotel to boot. The weather forecasters were predicting a cold, snowy few weeks to come, so hopefully there would be good skiing conditions in Austria. She had checked Bad Bergstein on Google and discovered that, like most Austrian resorts, it wasn't particularly high. According to a few online blogs she had found, it was not unheard of for the ski slopes at Christmas to be green rather than white. At least if she could get out and ski, she felt sure she would be able to put up with Grant's presence. The worst possible scenario would be a grey, rainy week when they would all be trapped in the confined space of the hotel together. She kept her fingers crossed.

She hadn't skied for several years now and she missed it. And it would be good to see her old university friends again – with or without Grant. However, there was always the article about Billy hanging over her head. Of course, she told herself, remembering the shy, retiring Billy of old, she might be able to persuade him to do an interview with her as an old friend and it might actually do something to help bolster his self-confidence. And, she told herself, she would do her best to make the piece kind, friendly, supportive, unlike some of the celebrity hatchet jobs that appeared in the media.

She hadn't mentioned the article to anybody, and she had no intention of doing so, but the thought of Billy made her comment to Juliet as they were trying on shoes, 'It's funny thinking of Computer Billy as a celebrity. Of all the people I knew back then, he's one of the last I could possibly have imagined. At uni, we hardly ever saw him and he rarely went out. I wonder if he's changed.'

'I was reading up about him and his company. Everybody says he's a bit of a mystery man. I couldn't even find a recent photo.'

'The *reclusive* Mr Fischer.'

'That's right. I imagine that means he's just the same. I wonder if he's still got those thick glasses.'

'Probably. You know, I don't think I ever saw him without them. I couldn't even tell you what colour his eyes are. In fact – and I know it sounds awful, seeing as he's offering us a wonderful free holiday – I don't really remember much about him at all.'

'I know what you mean. He lived in his room, ate in his room, worked in his room – round the clock, too. And when he did emerge, like a mole from its tunnel, he barely spoke a word.'

'He was a nice boy, though. On the few occasions we did exchange a few words, he was always very kind and eager to please. He was just so chronically shy. I bet he still is shy, and that's why they call him reclusive today.'

Juliet looked up from a pile of shoeboxes. 'You should offer to do a celebrity interview with him. That would be good for your career and it might be just what he needs to get him out of himself a bit more.'

Zoë couldn't stop the blood rushing to her cheeks, so she dropped her head and concentrated on removing the paper wads from the toes of a pair of gorgeous Italian shoes with far higher heels than she normally wore. As she did so, she mumbled, 'Good idea, Jules. I'll have to ask him if he's interested in something like that.'

At work on Friday, the subject came up again. Zoë found herself summoned to Damien's office mid morning to be introduced to a face she recognised, even though they had never met before.

'Zoë, I'd like you to meet a legend in the world of celebrity journalism. This is Crystal, from our New York office. She's over for a few days to interview Prince Harry. I've been telling her you've got an intro to the mysterious Mr Fischer from WF Computers, and I'm sure she'll be able to give you some useful advice about how to handle the very rich.'

As Zoë shook hands with the Ice Maiden, as Crystal liked to be known, her first impression was that the Maiden appellation was almost certainly misplaced. You didn't need to be Sigmund Freud to see that this lady had been round the block a good few times. Zoë knew her to be well into her fifties, but she was a masterpiece of the American cosmetic surgery industry. Anything worth nipping had been nipped. Tucks had been tucked and implants had been implanted. She had also probably emptied the poison sacs of a good number of unfortunate snakes in order to give her lips a Bardot pout and her cheeks the soft, smooth texture normally found on newborn children – or oil slicks. There wasn't a wrinkle on her. Her wrists and fingers were so laden down with gold jewellery, it was a wonder her arm muscles weren't bulging under the strain. From the immaculately styled hair, the perfect make-up and the designer clothes to the tips of her six-inch heels, she was every bit the queen of the celebrity press that she claimed to be. She couldn't have been more different from Zoë if she had just climbed out of a flying saucer.

'Zoë, great to meet you. Damien's been telling me wonderful things about you.'

Zoë felt the great lady give her a close forensic investigation. From the way her eyes bored into her, she felt sure Crystal had even noted her appendix scar and the fact that the labels on her underwear had started to fray. It was an uncomfortable feeling and she began to feel sorry for Prince Harry.

'And you're so beautiful, Zoë. That's marvellous. Use it. It's your most powerful weapon.'

'Not my brain?' Zoë did her best to keep the distaste she was feeling out of her voice.

'Listen, darling, this Mr Fischer is a man. Play to your strengths. A low-cut blouse can get through to a man far better than any number of incisive questions.'

Zoë shook her head in disbelief. 'Surely those days have passed? With all the hoo-ha about sexual predators nowadays, I would have thought we'd moved on a bit.'

'Don't you believe it, Zoë. Beneath the surface, all men are suckers for a nice-looking girl. Trust me, those're quite some assets you have there. Lock and load – and take no prisoners.'

Even Damien must have started to feel awkward at this point, in itself something of a rarity – shame and embarrassment were normally totally absent from his repertoire. He stood up and muttered that he had 'something to attend to' and hastened out of the office, leaving Zoë to face a half-hour masterclass on how to use feminine wiles to obtain pretty much anything from men. In Crystal's case, this had resulted in a penthouse apartment overlooking Central Park, a beach house in the Hamptons, and an Aston Martin.

After Zoë had finally shaken the Ice Maiden's immaculately manicured hand and left Damien's office, she stopped off in the ladies' to scrub her own hands under the tap before returning to her workstation. Her battered old car and her rented flat would do her just fine. Not for the first time, she determined to do her very best to find a new job as soon as one presented itself – as far from the world of celebrity journalism as possible.

Her mum and dad were in London that weekend, and she related her experiences with Crystal to them over an Indian takeaway that night. Her mother was predictably disgusted.

'Really! With everything you read in the papers and see on the TV these days, I thought those days were over. Don't you agree, Bernard?'

'Yes... yes, of course.'

Zoë's dad's answer was immediate, although Zoë thought she sensed a certain amount of scepticism.

'What is it, Dad? Do you think she's got a point?'

He shook his head. 'What, that you should flutter your eyelashes at this Billy in order to get him to reveal his deep dark secrets? Definitely not. The woman's attitude strikes me as repellent, but she has got a point to some extent. There's no getting away from it. However you look at it, men like pretty girls. You're a pretty girl, but you're a sensible girl. You won't do anything improper or stupid, I know.'

'Something as stupid as shacking up with a man who dumped me on Christmas Eve and went off with another woman?' There was a bitter edge to Zoë's voice.

'We all make mistakes, Zoë. Besides, you're better off without that Grant character, aren't you? Your mother and I never really liked him, you know.'

'But of course, you're going to see him at Christmas, aren't you, dear?' Her mum sounded concerned. 'Are you going to be all right?'

Zoë sighed. 'Everybody keeps asking me that. I'll be fine, I'm sure.'

Under the table, her fingers were, once again, firmly crossed.

Chapter 4

'Zoë, is that you?'

Zoë jumped at the sound of the voice. She had been vaguely listening to a choir singing carols over to one side of the check-in desks and wondering how her Austrian holiday would pan out. Her mood was a mixture of anticipation and dread. She turned and found two familiar faces looking at her – well, three really, although the only time she had seen the little girl before had been at her christening. And that was five years ago. She felt a smile forming on her face.

'Mandy, Martin, how great to see you. And this has to be Bella – wow, how she's grown.'

Zoë glanced around nervously, her eyes darting across the faces of the other passengers crowding into London Heathrow airport, but without recognising anybody else. It really was good to see her old student friends after so long, but the big unknown, of course, was going to be Grant. Over the months since replying to Billy's invitation, specifying that she would be coming alone, she had done her best to stifle thoughts of her ex and how she would react to seeing him – and his new woman. She had spent many nights dreaming of Christmas, but not with Juliet's sense of eager anticipation. In fact, on more than one occasion she had come very close to opening her laptop and emailing Billy to say she had changed her mind. Somehow she had remained resolute, but it had been a close-run thing. Yes, there would be a luxury hotel and the chance to go skiing again but, also, there would be Grant. Now that the big day had finally arrived, the apprehension she felt was almost overwhelming.

'Zoë, you look great.' Mandy dropped her bag and gave her a big hug. 'Come here, Bella, and say hello. This is Zoë. Daddy and I went to university with her.'

Somehow, seeing Mandy as a mother was totally in character. Even back at university, in the far-from-salubrious confines of number 23, she had always been the one to go to if you needed a plaster, a needle and thread, or just a hug.

Zoë swallowed her fears about her impending encounter with Grant and bent down to give the little girl a hug.

'Hello, Bella. The last time I saw you, you were just a tiny little baby. Look at you now! And you're the spitting image of your mother.'

She got a shy smile from the little girl in return, so she kissed her on the cheek and then straightened up and hugged Martin.

'Hi, Mart. You haven't changed a bit since I last saw you. Still as handsome as ever.'

He grinned back at her, revealing a double chin that hadn't been there before. He had grown a moustache as well, and that further aged him. Still, he didn't look too bad for an old fogey of over thirty – as they all were by now.

'And you're even more gorgeous than ever, Zoë. With your hair pinned up like that, you look very grown up.'

'I suppose we're all grown up now.' Zoë glanced past Martin's shoulder as she spotted two other familiar figures just coming into the terminal, pulling their bags behind them. 'And look who's here. It's Juliet and Lorna. Hi, Jules. Hi, Lorn – long time no see.'

'Hello, you lot.'

Lorna advanced upon their little group with open arms and hugged them all in turn. Juliet followed a little way behind and greeted them slightly less effusively. Zoë took a closer look at both of them. She had seen Juliet only a couple of weeks earlier, on their dress shopping expedition, and she was still looking fit, well and happy – although, as ever, a bit reticent, a bit shy. Lorna, on the other hand, was looking her age. There were dark rings under her eyes and Zoë wondered if these were a result of her still burning the candle at both ends, or whether she was unwell or feeling a bit down. She decided not to comment.

No sooner had they checked in than Lorna led them up to the bar and insisted on getting them to join her in a bottle of Prosecco, even though it was barely mid morning. Zoë accepted half a glass, as did the others, but Lorna soon disposed of the rest. As she drank, she talked non-stop, telling them about her new job and recounting her amorous exploits – of which there appeared to be too many to count. It was pretty clear that this particular leopard hadn't changed its spots, even if it was beginning to fray a bit around the edges.

Once Lorna had finally reached the end of her litany of paramours, the rest of them spent the next few hours at the airport and then on the short flight to Salzburg, reminiscing, exchanging notes and catching up on all the news. There was no sign of Grant and his woman, or of Imogen and her husband. Presumably they were on different flights. Although Zoë felt relieved not to find herself strapped into a seat alongside her ex, she knew the relief would only be short-lived. One way or another she was going to meet up with him soon, and the mixture of emotions coursing through her brain would have kept a psychiatrist fully occupied for hours.

She did her best to stay calm, and told them all about her job. She did not, of course, make any mention of Damien's article about Billy. The more she thought about it, the more distasteful it felt – a betrayal of trust that might not bother her editor, but which seriously worried her. She hastily moved the conversation on to Martin and Mandy.

Martin was doing well in his job – something to do with animal feeds – and he looked just as happy now as he had done all the way through university. He and Mandy had met in freshers' week and had been together ever since, and Zoë couldn't suppress a feeling of envy at the cosy family they now constituted with their little girl.

Juliet was still sounding upbeat, and she looked it too. Zoë listened as she updated the others on her life. She was still unattached, but she didn't appear to mind. She was playing squash and had bought herself a bike, and she felt very fit as a result. Zoë admitted that she too had been working out in the gym over the past few months, following a fairly rigorous exercise regime in the evenings after work, determined to be ready for skiing. Lorna, on the other hand, looked as if she would benefit from extending her aerobic activity outside of the bedroom.

They were well into their final descent towards Salzburg airport when Mandy asked the question that had been exercising Zoë's mind increasingly as the holiday had drawn closer.

'So, you and Grant? Are you going to be okay seeing him again?' She sounded concerned, and there was a serious expression on her face.

Zoë swallowed hard before replying, hoping that her determined air would fool the others. 'It'll be fine. A lot of time's passed and it's all water under the bridge now.'

For a second she caught Juliet's eye, then looked down hastily. Beside her, Mandy was still curious.

'Will this be the first time you've seen him since you split up?'

'Yes, but like I say, we're both grown-ups. It'll be fine.'

As she said it, Zoë found herself questioning her choice of words. Grant was still in many ways anything but grown up. His attitude towards life the last time she had seen him had still been as immature as when she had first met him. She wondered if his interests still centred on rugby, kitesurfing, snowboarding and beer. She mustered a smile.

'Anyway, I promise I won't do anything to spoil what's going to be a super holiday for everybody.'

Mandy gave her a sympathetic look.

'I heard that you'd split up, Zoë, but what happened? Why did you decide to go your separate ways, if you don't mind me asking?'

Zoë shook her head. 'No, of course I don't mind. It was very simple – I didn't decide anything. He did. He informed me over breakfast last Christmas Eve that he'd found somebody else and he wanted out.'

'He broke up with you at Christmas?'

'Great timing, eh?'

'What, just like that? No advance warning? Surely you must have suspected something.'

Zoë shook her head again. 'Nope. Nothing. At least, nothing serious.'

'Christmas must have been rough.'

'My mum and dad were great. I was a wreck, and if Mum hadn't been there, I'm sure I'd have burnt the turkey and probably set fire to the house. I suppose I was sort of in shock, really.'

'Damn right you were. How awful for you, and how callous of Grant.' Juliet didn't look like she was going to forgive him any time soon.

At that moment the aircraft bumped through the last of the clouds and the view opened up below them. Zoë saw a thick covering of snow on the roofs and, in spite of the memories that had been awakened and her qualms about seeing Grant again, she felt a surge of excitement. She was delighted to hear it in her voice as she finished answering Mandy's questions.

'But, you know something? I'm coming round to thinking it was maybe all for the best. Far better to make a clean break now, rather than discover his infidelities when I'm old and grey.'

She read considerable understanding and sympathy in Mandy's eyes and, encouraged, carried on with a fortitude in her voice that she didn't really feel.

'Anyway, let's try not to make this holiday about me and Grant. What about you lot? Are you looking forward to skiing?'

Across the aisle, she saw Lorna shake her head.

'Not me. I'm here for the five-star luxury and the rich men. It's amazing how a well-stuffed wallet makes a man so much more attractive.'

She was grinning, but Zoë got the feeling she probably wasn't joking. She returned her attention to Mandy.

'And you, Mand?'

'Definitely – although I don't know if I'll actually put on skis. I'm looking forward to the mountain air and the chance to have a rest and put my feet up.' She pointed to her daughter. 'Bella and Martin have been taking lessons on the dry ski slope.' At the sound of her name, the little girl leant forward in her seat and looked past her mother towards Zoë.

'Daddy's pretty rubbish, but I'm ever so good.'

'Good for you, Bella. I look forward to skiing with you all.' Zoë looked out of the window again. 'They say the snow conditions are the best for years. We should be able to ski from the hotel right to the lifts and back again.'

The *Fasten Seat Belts* sign lit up and they began their final approach. Looking out of the window, it was clear that they were flying up a valley to reach Salzburg airport, and the wingtips rose and fell scarily as the aircraft yawed from side to side, following the meanderings of the river below. As they landed, they could all see from the piles of snow alongside the runway that the recent snowfall had been heavy. The weathermen had been dead right about the terrific skiing conditions that awaited them.

Once they had collected their luggage, half deafened by non-stop Christmas songs blaring out of the loudspeakers, they emerged from the restricted area of the airport and found a smart gentleman in a dark suit waiting to greet them. In his leather-gloved hands he was holding a sign marked *Grand Hotel Schlossberg*. As he led them outside, he explained in excellent English that their journey to the hotel should take just over an hour. It had indeed snowed heavily for the past three days, but he reassured them that the main roads were now all clear. Zoë reflected what effect half a metre of snow would have had on the British roads – chaos for a week, probably.

The first part of the journey was on a good motorway, heading due south along a wide valley that gradually narrowed. The snow-covered mountains formed a stunning backdrop ahead of them. The road surface had indeed been meticulously cleared and, as at the airport, there were huge banks of snow at the roadside, testifying to the recent work of the snowploughs. Gradually the slopes left and right of them became steeper and the scenery more spectacular. The valley walls were now sheer cliffs and the river alongside the road was iced over. There was deep snow everywhere. Houses and farms looked as if they were half buried under a thick white blanket.

After a while, they turned off to the left and headed up another valley, which climbed gradually through the snow-covered pines. The sky had now cleared and there wasn't a cloud to be seen. Amazingly, there was a railway line alongside the road and the driver informed them that the tracks disappeared into a tunnel at the head of the valley, but that Bad Bergstein was a few miles before that. The views as the road snaked its way up the valley were stunning, with glimpses of white peaks high above them. As they approached their destination, the valley widened out and they began to spot ski lifts and distant figures skiing through the fir trees on both sides of the valley.

Bad Bergstein was a very smart old ski resort, with many of the buildings probably dating back to the heyday of the Austro-Hungarian Empire. Some of the houses were rather fine fin-de-siècle residences, while others were more traditional chalet-style buildings made of weathered wood, or with white walls and dark wooden balconies. The sloping roofs collected and held the snow as an extra layer of insulation. After the recent snowfall, they looked like iced cakes.

As their driver took them past a small lake, now completely frozen over, Zoë could see figures skating on it or strolling around the edges, enjoying the last rays of the afternoon sun. They drove on up a gently sloping road lined with shops and hotels, and everywhere they looked they saw people wearing brightly coloured skiing clothes stomping about in heavy boots. She felt a shiver of excitement at the thought of getting back on skis once more. Christmas lights and decorations hung everywhere, and she heard Bella and her mum counting no fewer than six big Christmas trees on the pavements. She glanced over at the little girl, whose eyes were shining. She had almost forgotten how exciting this time of year was for children, and it brought a smile to her own face, in spite of the prospect of what, or rather who, awaited her at the hotel.

By the time they reached their hotel, the views had changed from lovely to spectacular. The mountains were all around them, with the peaks of the Tauern Alps clearly visible against the darkening sky in the distance. Ski runs weaved in and out of the snow-laden fir trees, and the occasional old wooden hut or barn poked up from the white covering that threatened to submerge it. There were still skiers on the slopes, but it would be dark before long and the lifts would soon stop. Zoë found herself hoping the pistes wouldn't be too crowded, although as Christmas was in just seven days' time, things would no doubt get busier and busier.

The hotel in the flesh was every bit as impressive as the website had indicated. The rows of wooden balconies formed dark horizontal lines across the front of the big white building, giving it a very traditional Austrian look, and the roof with its wide overhanging eaves was covered with a thick coat of snow. Dusk was falling and the trees alongside the drive and in front of the entrance had been strung with sparkling lights. There was a huge Christmas tree right outside the main entrance, decked with silver and gold baubles. It looked very festive, very beautiful and very welcoming. From behind her, Martin spoke for just about the first time.

'Wow, what a place!'

His daughter joined in, sounding equally impressed.

'It's beautiful. Look, Mummy. It's wonderful.'

Mandy smiled at her. 'I know, it's like something out of a fairy tale.'

Zoë gave Bella a grin. 'Maybe there's a handsome prince in there, waiting for you.' As she spoke, the image of Grant appeared uninvited before her eyes and she shook her head to clear her thoughts. 'I think we're going to love it here.'

'Take a look at the flashy cars in the car park. Bound to be loads of lovely rich men, just you wait and see.' Lorna sounded distinctly predatory, and Zoë saw Mandy roll her eyes.

The minibus drew up right outside the main entrance and the driver came round to open the doors.

'Just leave your luggage. It will all be brought to your rooms.'

Zoë and Juliet exchanged glances. Yes, this was going to be a special holiday.

'If you'd like to follow my colleague, he will take you inside.'

A man in a white shirt and a bright green waistcoat appeared at the glass doors and came hurrying down the steps to greet them.

'*Grüss Gott, meine Damen und Herren.*' He gave them a smile. 'Welcome to the Schlossberg. If you would like to come with me...' He stood to one side and they followed the direction of his outstretched hand.

As the glass doors hissed open, they walked up the steps, past a couple of ski racks and into a high-ceilinged, spacious lobby with a sparkling ultra-modern chandelier. There was a massive Christmas tree at one end and the reception desk was positioned along the left-hand side. The place was a winter wonderland. The wood-panelled walls were festooned with holly branches and shiny silver baubles, alongside huge heart-shaped ornaments studded with pine cones. Garlands of pine and fir branches hung from the ceiling and a dozen smaller trees in pots were lined up against the walls, giving the impression of entering a magical forest. A lingering scent of cinnamon hung in the air, and all around there were oranges and cinnamon sticks on display. On the counter was a tray of chocolate and marzipan confectionery in various Christmas shapes, and even the staff behind the reception desk had entered into the Christmas spirit, with plastic reindeer antlers on their heads. Even the manager, impeccable in a dark suit, was wearing an elf's hat. The place was wonderfully warm, and exuded elegance and comfort. Zoë gave a little sigh of appreciation. It certainly made a wonderful change from her flat, which was decidedly spartan in comparison.

'Go straight across to the lift, please.'

The smiley man in the green waistcoat led them past the reception desk and ushered them into the lift. Even this had been decorated and the ivy, baubles and pine cones around the door made it look as if they were entering Santa's grotto. He pressed the button for the top floor, and the doors closed silently behind him. There was almost no sensation of movement as they were whisked up to the sixth floor. The only sound was a discreet chime as they reached their destination and the door opened.

'This floor is exclusively for the use of your party. Erika here will look after you, and if there's anything you require, she or I will be delighted to help.'

There was a smaller version of the steel and glass reception desk right opposite the lift, and behind it was another smiling face, this time belonging to a dark-haired girl in a white dirndl blouse with a tight green bodice. She was wearing a red and white Santa hat on her head and alongside her on the counter stood a bushy little Christmas tree, decked with tinsel and twinkling with fairy lights. Bella gazed at the scene in wonder, eyes wide open, mouth gaping.

Erika greeted them in excellent English.

'Good afternoon and welcome. If I could just ask you for your documents, I'll show you to your rooms. And those of you who need ski passes, please let me know and I'll get them organised.'

Once they had produced their passports, Erika took them on a brief tour of the floor. It was clear that they were up in the eaves, as the timber ceilings supported by hefty wooden beams sloped away on either side of the central corridor. The first room they saw — a fine, airy room with a big table in the middle and other chairs and tables dotted around the sides — was on their left, looking out towards the rear of the hotel. Here, too, the Christmas theme was repeated, with a tree hung with enough chocolate baubles to satisfy even the hungriest glutton. As they passed it, Erika plucked a huge chocolate star off the tree and handed it to Bella.

'*Fröhliche Weihnachten*. Happy Christmas.'

Without needing to be prompted by her mother, Bella gave her a beaming smile and thanked her, as Erika continued her introduction.

'In here is your private dining room. You can take your breakfast here or in your rooms — as you wish. Breakfast is normally served between seven and ten, but if you prefer a different time, please just let me know.' She waved vaguely in the direction of a bar with an array of bottles on display. 'Everything is complimentary, so do help yourselves. If you want hot drinks or anything else, please tell me and I'll get them sent up for you. There is a larger choice of alcoholic and non-alcoholic drinks in the main bar in your private lounge. Of course, there are tea- and coffee-making facilities in your rooms as well.'

Zoë and Juliet exchanged glances and Juliet mouthed the word, *Wow*.

Erika glanced down at Bella, who had already stuffed most of the chocolate star into her cheeks and looked like a little hamster. She smiled at the girl.

'And you are very welcome to eat the chocolates on the tree, but only if your mother says it's okay.'

Mandy smiled at her daughter. 'Just one a day, Bella. All right?'

The little girl nodded, incapable of answering because her mouth was so full. Erika grinned and went on.

'At the end of the corridor is the lounge, again just for your group. As Georg said, William specifically wanted this whole floor to be at your disposal.'

So William was presumably Billy, Zoë thought to herself. He must be well known to them here at the hotel if they addressed him by his first name. Mind you, anybody shelling out for a whole floor of a luxury hotel at Christmas time would no doubt be well known to the staff.

'I'll show you to your rooms now. I'm afraid it's getting a bit too dark for skiing tonight, but if you want the pool, the thermal baths or the fitness centre, you can find them on the lower ground floor. One of my colleagues will provide you with towels down there, and you'll find there are changing facilities.'

Erika pointed along the corridor.

'If you feel like meeting the rest of your party after I've shown you to your rooms, there's afternoon tea and champagne waiting for you in the lounge.'

Zoë looked across at the others and saw the expressions of awe on all their faces. This was certainly a far cry from the last time they had lived side-by-side together, at number 23. Her lasting memories of that house had been the damp, the cold and the resident rodent population.

Chapter 5

Zoë's room was enormous, with a huge double bed almost submerged beneath a thick duvet, whose pristine white cotton cover made it look for all the world like a deep layer of snow. The walls were wood-panelled and there were two big windows. There was tinsel, hung with silver baubles, around the mirror and a bowl of fresh fruit and chocolates on the side. A stylish sofa stood against one wall, facing a huge flat-screen television, and there was a reading desk and chair in the far corner. Zoë walked across and looked out of the window. Even in the twilight, the view was amazing. She could see all the way over the dark mass of the town to the outline of the hills on the far side of the valley. The square tower of the church with its elegant steeple was just about the only roof without a covering of snow – the pitch was just too steep. In the distance off to her left was the massive bulk of the high mountains, occasional outcrops of rock showing up as dark stains against the smooth covering of snow. It was a stunning view and she was still standing there when she heard a soft tap on the door.

'Your bags, madam.'

She hurried across to open the door and a different man in a green waistcoat carried her suitcase in and set it down on a solid bench against one wall. Zoë was still reaching into her handbag for her purse to give him a tip when he retraced his footsteps to the door and disappeared with just two words.

'Goodbye, madam.'

'*Auf wiedersehen, danke.*'

It felt good to speak German again. She had done French and German at school and she had particularly liked German. There was something about the rigid mechanical structure of the sentences that appealed to her sense of organisation. She found she was looking forward to a bit of practice – assuming she managed to find an Austrian who didn't already speak fluent English.

She hung up her jacket and inspected the bathroom, which was ultra-modern, predictably immaculate, and almost as big as the bedroom she and Grant had shared at number 23. Thick towels were stacked on a rack and a fluffy white bathrobe with the hotel crest on the left breast hung on the back of the door. She checked herself in the mirror, washed her hands and decided to go and look for the others. And among the others, of course, would be Grant and his companion. She took a deep breath as she pulled her door closed behind her and set off down the corridor towards the lounge.

She was only partway along the corridor when she was almost tripped by a black flash. Looking down, she saw the most adorable young black Labrador scrabbling at her shoes, tail wagging furiously.

'Arnie, come back here.'

She turned in the direction of the familiar voice and saw a figure coming down the corridor towards her, arms outstretched in welcome. The dog made no attempt to do as ordered and continued to nuzzle Zoë's feet, scratching at her shoes with his disproportionately large paws.

'Billy, is that you?'

She realised that she wasn't totally sure it was him. Billy, Computer Billy, had been recognisable by his unkempt hair and thick black-rimmed glasses, and his habit of always wearing two T-shirts – the inner one with long sleeves and the outer one with short sleeves, normally bearing the image of a superhero on the chest. The man coming towards her with a nervous smile on his lips was wearing a beautiful grey mohair V-neck jumper. He had no glasses, and his brown hair was impeccably styled, just touching the tops of his ears. He also looked altogether taller and quite a lot broader in the shoulders than the nerdy boy she remembered. If this was Billy, he'd had a serious makeover.

'Zoë, how wonderful to see you.'

It really was him.

'And it's great to see you, too, Billy.'

It was patently obvious that her theory that he might be keeping a low public profile because he was still a scruffy nerd had just been blown out of the water. She stepped towards him, tripped over the dog, who had by now stretched himself across her feet, and literally fell into Billy's arms. As he caught her, she couldn't help feeling how strong his biceps had become. He'd obviously been working out.

'Arnie, you little bugger, get out of the way.'

Billy gave her a peck on both cheeks and then stepped back, studying her closely, the slightly nervous smile still on his face.

'It really is great to see you.' He sounded as if he meant it. 'And you haven't lost your knack for tripping over things, I see.'

'I'm getting better – honest. It's great to see you too. You're looking good, Billy.' And he was. In fact, if she hadn't been expecting to see him, she would almost certainly have walked past without recognising him. There was genuine surprise in her voice as she asked: 'What happened to the old Billy?'

He released his hold on her and bent down to dissuade the dog from tearing her shoes to pieces.

'Sorry about Arnie, he's going through the chewing phase at the moment. He's got a thing about shoes.'

He straightened up again, his smile still a bit uncertain.

'As for the old Billy, he's still in here, even if the exterior has changed a bit.' He grinned. 'Believe me, it's just a veneer – you'll see. Underneath the new hairstyle – when I say "new", I just mean hairstyle. There was no style involved back when we lived at number 23. I waited until the hair got in my eyes and then chopped it off. Anyway, underneath the new hairstyle and the contact lenses, there's still little old me. But you, Zoë, you look just as beautiful as you did ten years ago – as if nothing has changed.'

He must have spotted something in her expression.

'But of course lots of things have changed for you, haven't they? How're you doing? I heard a rumour that you and Grant had split up, and when you both opted for single rooms, I realised it was true.'

Zoë felt an immediate sense of relief. It appeared that Grant was not, after all, going to be accompanied by his new partner. Suddenly her whole Christmas looked rosier.

She had been dreading having to spend a week in close confines with the other woman, knowing that inevitably her friends would be making comparisons between the two of them. This was the very best news she could have hoped for – apart, of course, from Grant maybe deciding to change his mind about coming at the last minute. But even though he evidently *was* still coming, the fact that he would be on his own came as a great relief. Fortified by this discovery, she was able to give Billy a big smile and reply in a fairly strong voice.

'You're right. We've split up.' She wondered idly how he had heard about their break-up. Clearly the bush telegraph must extend all the way to Austria. 'I'm afraid it all fell apart a year ago. In fact almost exactly a year ago.'

'I'm so sorry.' He shook his head sadly. 'You were together for a long time, weren't you? I thought it was a relationship that would last.'

'So did I, Billy. So did I.' As casually as she could, she did a little bit of digging. 'So, did Grant say why he's here alone?'

Billy shook his head. 'No, not really. He didn't mention anybody. I'll have to ask him.'

'Not that it's of any importance to me any more.' Determined to stay upbeat, Zoë took his arm and gave it a squeeze. She saw him blush and realised he had been speaking the truth – underneath the well-groomed and, yes, handsome exterior, he was still timid old Billy. Her heart went out to him.

'Anyway, all this is so very, very generous of you, Billy. It's a fabulous place and I'm so terribly grateful.'

He brushed away her thanks.

'Don't even think about it. I've had some good luck and the least I can do is share it with my old friends. I'm just delighted you accepted my invitation. Now, let's go down to the lounge. Imogen and Fergus arrived a couple of hours ago, and Daniela, my wife, will be here a bit later.'

Zoë glanced up at him in real surprise.

'Congratulations, Billy. I didn't know you'd got married. That's fantastic.'

As she spoke, she reflected that she had never even seen him with a girl when they were living at number 23. He had always had his nose buried in his computer. Mind you, that lifestyle choice certainly appeared to have worked out well for him. And, she thought to herself, this was already a juicy piece of news for her article – as long as Billy didn't mind. She had decided, even if she felt sure Damien and the Ice Maiden would disapprove, that she would come clean and tell him what her editor had asked and get his approval, before sending anything back to the office. It was only right and proper.

'So tell me about Arnie the dog. Is he yours?'

As she asked the question, she felt mildly surprised that a luxury hotel like this allowed pets in the rooms.

'He is now, though originally he belonged to my aunt here in Austria. She only got him in the summer, and then she died very unexpectedly three months ago. I said I'd take him for a few days after her death – and look at me now.'

'I'm sorry to hear about your aunt. What does your wife think about having a pup in the house to chew up all her lovely shoes?'

For a moment Billy looked surprised. 'She doesn't mind. We've both got into the habit of putting everything away. In fact, having Arnie about the place has made me a hell of a lot tidier.' He led her along the corridor. 'So, here's the lounge. Did Erika tell you this floor's just for our group?'

Zoë nodded as he pushed the door open and ushered her inside. She took a deep breath as she did so, expecting to see Grant in there. Instead, she only found Imogen and a man who was presumably her husband.

As soon as Imogen spotted Zoë, she leapt to her feet and came hurrying across.

'Zoë, how lovely to see you again after all this time.'

She took hold of Zoë's hands and air-kissed her theatrically before turning to introduce the friendly-looking man beside her. He was maybe a year or two older than them, and he was somewhat overdressed for a skiing holiday, wearing a smart dark suit and a tie bearing some kind of crest on it. Zoë nodded to herself – this was pretty much what she had been expecting. Imogen wasn't the type to hitch herself to a jeans-and-jumper man. She herself was looking predictably elegant. Zoë knew very little about fashion, but she felt sure the dress Imogen was wearing would prove to have a designer label. Imogen had always been flashy like that – 'all fur coat and no knickers', as Zoë's grandmother would have said.

'And this is Fergus, my husband. We got married three years ago. I would have invited you, but I've lost touch a bit.'

With social media these days, it would have been easy enough for Imogen to contact her, but Zoë made no comment. They hadn't really been that close at university, so there was no reason she should have been invited to the wedding. She gave Fergus a smile and shook his outstretched hand.

'Zoë, how good to meet you.' There was a definite Scottish accent there – the sort of accent that inhabits the upper-class areas of Edinburgh rather than the shipyards of the Clyde. 'Imogen's told me so much about you.'

'And Grant?' Imogen was looking beyond Zoë and Billy.

'Zoë and Grant split up a year ago,' Billy stepped in to explain, and Zoë was grateful to him for his intervention. 'Grant is here – he arrived on the Manchester flight early this morning – but he went snowboarding this afternoon and he hasn't come back yet.'

Yet again, Zoë felt a sense of relief, even though she knew this was merely putting off the inevitable.

She took a good look round the room. It was a big space, dominated by a magnificent stove in one corner. This was almost the size of a wardrobe and made of decorative blue and white ceramic tiles. The heat coming off it made the room very, very cosy, and she noticed the dog make a beeline straight for the rug laid out in front of it.

The rest of the room was charming, with fine-looking Persian carpets on the floor and stylish paintings hanging around the walls. There was a delightful Christmas tree, festooned with silver and gold baubles, in the opposite corner, and a sprig of mistletoe hung from the chandelier in the middle of the room. All around were comfortable-looking sofas and armchairs, and two tables against the wall behind them were loaded with cakes and biscuits, with many Austrian specialities. Zoë recognised sugar-sprinkled apple strudel, a delicious-looking Stollen, and a pile of pancakes, but some of the other delights on display were unfamiliar and intriguing.

'Blimey, Billy. I can see that all the hard work I've been doing in the gym is going to be undone pretty quickly.'

'It's Christmas, Zoë. Let yourself go.'

She looked up to see him smiling shyly at her.

'Besides, if you feel like going out on the ski slopes, you'll soon burn it off. It's minus five or six outside in the mornings, and you'll need a good few calories inside you just to keep out the cold.'

'I certainly intend to do as much skiing as I can. What about you, Billy, do you ski?'

He nodded. 'Yes, since we set up our centre of operations here in Austria, I've been doing quite a bit of it. Besides, I have relatives in Kitzbühel and I used to spend several weeks every year with them.'

'I never knew that.'

Zoë reflected that really she knew very little about him. Although they had lived under the same roof for a year, she had spoken to him infrequently – not because she didn't like him, but because of his shyness and the fact that he spent so much of his time in his room, working at the computer. For her own sake, as much as for her article, she set out to find out more.

'Your surname, Fischer with a "c" – does that mean you have Austrian roots?'

Billy nodded. 'My grandparents were Austrian, but they moved across to Britain after the war.'

'And did you grow up speaking German?'

'Not much at home, but every time I came here on holiday, I had to speak it.'

'So you honed your German at the same time as your skiing. Good plan.'

'And you're a good skier too, I believe?' He caught her eye for a moment. 'At least, that's what Grant told me this morning.'

'I'm a bit out of practice, but yes, I do okay.'

'We'll have to ski together then.' Billy turned to Imogen and Fergus. 'What about you two? Do you ski?'

'Fergus does. To be honest, I'd rather sit and watch.'

Imogen clearly hadn't changed. She had never been interested in exercise, and indeed, had sneered at anybody who was. This attitude had not endeared her to Grant, who had spent far more of his time playing sport than studying for his finals. The thought of Grant made Zoë glance across at the door, and just as she did so, she saw the handle turn. Her heart leapt – whether in anticipation or apprehension she didn't have time to decide. As she looked on, the door opened and a figure appeared – but it wasn't Grant.

Instead, a very tall, slim, athletic-looking girl maybe a year or two younger than the rest of them stepped into the room. She was extremely beautiful, with long dark hair hanging around her shoulders, and she was wearing an expensive top and black yoga pants. When she saw Billy, her face broke into a smile, and she came across to greet him with a tender kiss on the cheek.

'*Ciao*, Billy.'

She had more than a hint of an Italian accent. Billy beamed at her and made the introductions.

'Come and say hello to my old university friends. You guys, this is my wife, Daniela.'

As Daniela did the rounds, shaking hands with everybody, Zoë checked her out. Apart from being very beautiful, it was clear that she thought the world of her husband, draping herself across him once she had said hello to them all. The expression on her face when she looked at him was brimming with love, and Zoë felt a twinge of envy at their happiness. Of course, she thought to herself rather cattily, the fact that Billy was a multimillionaire probably helped. Doing her best to put aside such churlish thoughts, she engaged Daniela in conversation.

'So, how long have you two been married?' She grinned. 'And why wasn't I invited to the wedding?'

Daniela blushed and deferred to her husband.

Billy shook his head. '*Nobody* was invited to the wedding, Zoë. We wanted to keep it a big secret. The trouble with being in the public eye is that once the paparazzi latch onto you, they never let you alone. I didn't want to put Daniela through that.' He smiled. 'A little bird tells me you work for *HC* magazine. You won't spill the beans, will you? I've worked really hard to try to maintain my privacy. You haven't been sent to spy on me, have you?'

Zoë blushed. 'No, of course not…'

'I'm just messing with you, Zoë. I know you'd never do anything like that. To be honest, though, I'm surprised that you're working for a bunch like that. You've always been such a principled sort of person.'

Zoë gulped. 'And I still am, Billy. It's a stopgap – I lost my previous job as a real journalist back in the spring.' She did her best not to let the colour rush to her cheeks. Luckily, Imogen took over the questioning.

'And how did you two meet?'

This time Daniela answered, and from the way she spoke, it was clear this wasn't the first time she had told the story.

'Billy gave me a job first, and proposed marriage afterwards.' She smiled at their mystification. 'He employed me as his personal trainer, and the more time we spent together, the closer we became.'

'By the time she'd got my abs and my pecs into shape, I'd fallen in love with her.' Billy kissed her gently on the cheek. 'We got married three months ago in a secret location.' He grinned. 'But I can tell you guys – it was here in this very room.'

'I thought Erika at the reception desk seemed to know you well,' Zoë smiled at him. 'You must be a regular visitor.'

For a moment, there was a glimpse of the old bashful Billy as he answered.

'To be quite honest, I actually own the hotel.' Seeing their expressions of incredulity, he hastened to explain. 'My accountants told me I should diversify my portfolio, so, seeing as our European base is now in Austria and I like skiing, it seemed like a good idea.'

Here was yet another gem for Zoë's article – if he ever approved her writing it.

'So do you live here?'

'I keep the suite at the end of the corridor for myself, but I've got a house down in Salzburg, which is where our offices are.'

'Fancy owning a hotel…' Imogen's tone was awestruck. 'It's such a gorgeous place.'

'I'm glad you like it.'

Zoë was unsurprised to see Imogen gazing covetously across at Billy – or rather at his money. She cast a surreptitious glance at Imogen's husband and caught a look of discomfort and maybe even annoyance on his face. She shook her head slowly. At least, she thought to herself, if Imogen and Fergus started having marital problems, it would divert attention from her own relationship issues with Grant.

A few minutes later, Juliet arrived with Martin, Mandy and Bella. Not surprisingly, the little girl was immediately drawn first to the pup and then to the cakes and biscuits, and they all followed suit – including the Labrador. As they did so, Lorna arrived, freshly changed into remarkably conservative clothes, rather than the more outrageous outfits Zoë remembered her wearing back at number 23. She wondered if Lorna was planning to maintain her high-octane private life, or if a change was due. None of them was getting any younger, after all. Even Zoë herself, in spite of her protestations that she wasn't interested in another man after the Grant debacle, had spent long hours wondering if she was somehow destined to end up on her own. It was an uncomfortable thought.

She helped herself to a cup of tea and a slice of Stollen, but Lorna headed straight for the champagne and several of the others joined her. The prospect of a completely open bar was alluring, but Zoë was determined to take it slow. She wanted to have a good time, but she wanted to be able to remember it.

'I'm especially glad you could come, Jules.' Billy glanced over towards Juliet, who was standing to one side looking even more timid than he did. 'Apart from the pleasure of seeing you again, I'm sure we're all greatly cheered to know that we've got a real medical doctor with us, in case of accidents. Come over here and tell us all about life in a big hospital.'

Zoë saw a smile appear on Juliet's face and was very impressed at Billy's ability to get her involved. The old Billy would, if anything, have been hiding behind Juliet. He really had undergone an impressive change, even if she now knew that the old timid Billy was still lurking not far below the surface.

They stood around chatting for a good while as the light faded outside and darkness fell. Zoë nibbled the delicious Stollen, the traditional Germanic Christmas cake. It was filled with candied peel and dried fruit, and emanated a wonderful aroma of cinnamon. It was soft, fresh and gorgeous. After talking to Daniela about her exercise programme, she spent some time with Lorna, doing her best to assess just what was going on inside her head. At university, Grant had described Lorna as being 'the proverbial good time had by all', and she had unquestionably earned herself a reputation as a man-eater. Now, however, Zoë somehow began to get the feeling that beneath the good-time-girl bluster, Lorna was maybe no longer quite so flighty. Zoë had always liked her, in spite of the excesses of her voracious sexual appetite, and she resolved to sit down and have a longer chat with her sometime this week.

As six o'clock came and went, Zoë decided she could allow herself some champagne – not least to help her nerves as the time of her reunion with Grant approached. She helped herself to a glass and sat down to stroke the dog, who seemed to have taken a liking to her and had settled himself at her feet – mercifully no longer trying to attack her shoes. She was just taking a sip when she heard the door open, and this time, when she looked up, she saw that the moment she had been dreading had finally arrived.

Grant stopped in the doorway, eyes scouring the room until he saw her. Without hesitation – ignoring everybody else in the room – he came straight across to her, and for a moment, it looked as though he was going to bend down and kiss her. Zoë recoiled, losing control of her glass, spilling champagne onto the Labrador and sending her mouthful down the wrong way. As she dissolved into a coughing fit, she saw the dog spring to his feet, shaking the wine off his back, and fix her with a puzzled look that was perfectly reflected in the eyes of the man standing above him. As she spotted the similarity, she felt a rising sense of the absurd, and her coughing fit swiftly turned into an attack of the giggles.

'Zoë, are you all right?'

Grant sounded concerned and puzzled. If the Labrador had been able to speak, she felt sure he would have asked the same question.

As she wiped her eyes and did her best to regain some semblance of control, she saw Juliet march over to her assistance.

'Good evening, Grant. Zoë's just fine.'

Juliet's tone was far from cordial, as was her expression. This demonstration of support further cheered Zoë, and when she finally regained the power of speech, she found she was able to reply quite confidently.

'Hello, Grant.' She made no attempt to get up or to offer him even a handshake. Instead, she kept her attention on Arnie, stroking him as he slid down her ankles to the floor and rolled over on his back, paws waving in the air.

There was an awkward pause, and then she heard Grant's voice again.

'Let me get you a refill.'

She felt him remove her now empty glass from her hand and saw his feet disappear towards the refreshment tables. Only now did she raise her head. Juliet was standing over her protectively, a concerned look on her face.

'Feeling okay?' Juliet kept her voice low, although Grant was across at the other side of the room by now.

Zoë gave her a grateful smile.

'Better than expected, thanks, Jules. I'm fine now. Just my usual butterfingers, I'm afraid. You know what I'm like when it comes to spilling stuff.'

'Under the circumstances, I'd say that was excusable. Anyway, remember I'm here if you need me.'

When Grant returned with fresh champagne, he was accompanied by Billy, who gave Zoë an encouraging wink as he sought to ease any awkwardness by changing the subject.

'There's more snow forecast overnight tonight. Tomorrow should be perfect skiing conditions, although I'm afraid I have to go down to Salzburg for a series of meetings, more's the pity. Anyway, don't forget, Erika will have your ski passes later on tonight and you can pick up skis and boots from the shop directly opposite the hotel in the morning. They'll be expecting you, so just give them your names and they'll sort you out.' He turned towards Grant. 'How did you find it on the slopes this afternoon?'

By now, Zoë was feeling much less worried, and to a great extent this was because she could see that Grant

– normally so self-confident – was looking even more nervous than she had been. In fact he sounded quite tongue-tied as he mumbled a brief reply to Billy's question.

'Erm, great, super.'

The realisation that he had probably been just as anxious about their reunion as she had was very reassuring. Somehow she had been expecting to find him displaying his usual cocky air. Seeing him like a shy teenager, with a nervous smile playing on the corners of his lips, did wonders for her confidence. It also considerably reduced the fear she had had that she might decide to pick something up and hit him with it.

She deliberately ignored him as she made her apologies to her host.

'Billy, I'm sorry for spilling that lovely champagne – you know me… But I see Arnie's licked most of it up. Can dogs get drunk?'

'Normal dogs, maybe. This one's got the constitution of a goat. He'd probably drink the whole lot and then crunch up the bottle itself and swallow the pieces without batting an eyelid.' Billy grinned at her, then glanced down benevolently at the dog. 'He ate a perfectly good leather glove the other day, and managed to expel it the other end without any apparent discomfort – although it didn't do the glove any good at all. Quite amazing. So, do you like the champagne? It's from a little place near Epernay. I got them to ship me a dozen cases specially for this week.'

Zoë took a sip and nodded appreciatively.

'It's amazing – just like the rest of this place. Thanks so much for having us.'

'You are so very welcome.'

'Zoë, is it all right if Bella and I come and sit with you?'

Zoë looked up at the sound of Mandy's voice. She, too, had clearly decided to join Juliet in a concerted show of solidarity in the face of Grant.

'Of course, I'd be delighted.'

'Grant, you haven't met my wife yet, have you?' Clearly Billy was still in full diplomatic mode. Zoë saw him lay a hand on Grant's shoulder and steer him to the other side of the room, and yet again, she reflected on the change their once nerdy friend appeared to have undergone.

She looked up and caught Mandy's eye as she and her daughter sat down on the sofa alongside her.

'Thanks, Mand.' Zoë straightened up and transferred her attention to the little girl. 'So, Bella, what do you think of this place?'

'It's wonderful. And I like the doggy. Do you like dogs, Zoë?'

By this time, Arnie had stretched himself out over Zoë's feet again and was making happy little canine grunts as he licked champagne off his forelegs. Zoë nodded.

'I love them. We never had one at home because my mum's allergic – you know, she gets all itchy if she touches a dog – but I've always wanted one. Sooner or later, when I settle down with a home of my own, I know I'll get a dog.'

'Haven't you got a home of your own now?'

'Well, yes, but there's just me there. I meant when – if – I have a family.' She found her eyes straying involuntarily across the room to the corner where Grant was deep in conversation with Daniela and Billy.

'Haven't you got a family either?'

Bella would no doubt make a great counsel for the prosecution in years to come if she carried on like this.

'Um, no. I mean, I've got my mum and dad, but I don't live with them.' Zoë smiled. She had forgotten how inquisitive little kids could be.

'Why don't you live with them?'

'Because my job's in London and they live in Bath.'

'Why do they live in the bath?'

At this point, Bella's mother intervened to bale Zoë out.

'It's a place, darling. Now, tell Zoë all about your skiing lessons. I'm sure she's dying to hear how you got on.'

–

Dinner that night was excellent. Zoë had never visited Austria before and she wasn't quite sure what to expect. In fact, the meal was very cosmopolitan, with Italian bresaola, air-dried beef served with flakes of Parmesan cheese, Hungarian sausage, and local wild mushrooms in olive oil as a starter, and then piping-hot beef stew with British-style cauliflower cheese as a main course. They drank excellent dry white Austrian Grüner Veltliner and specially imported Gigondas red from Provence with the meal. The dessert was an Austrian speciality, and it was really, really good. Billy told them it was called *Kaiserschmarrn* – a sort of lightly fried sweet pancake made with raisins, shredded into rough pieces, sprinkled with sugar and served with a hot plum sauce. It tasted wonderful, and in spite of her resolve to take it easy with the food and drink, Zoë devoured a big portion. She wondered how many calories there were in something like this, but preferred not to ask.

As it turned out, they needed all the calories they had consumed. At the end of the meal, Billy tapped his glass shyly and announced that he had arranged a little tour for them after dinner if they felt like it – and they all did. This turned out to be in horse-drawn sledges through the narrow streets of the old town, and it was a memorable experience.

The horses were all decked out for Christmas, with embroidered coats on their backs and feathery head-dresses. Even the drivers were wearing Father Christmas hats and white beards – either real or fake. The passengers were provided with heavy blankets to put over their knees, and they needed them, even though they were all wearing warm winter clothing. As Zoë's eyes got used to the darkness, she realised that the white covering of snow everywhere meant that she could see her surroundings really quite easily. The sky was still clear, in spite of the forecast of snow, and the stars were twinkling in all their glory, their light reflecting back up from the snow-covered ground. The stars might have been orbs of superheated burning gas, but down here on earth it was very, very cold.

There were two sledges, with space for up to six people in each – three facing forwards, three backwards. Zoë was relieved to see Grant get into the first one, along with Imogen and her husband, Mandy, Martin and little Bella. In the second one, Zoë found herself sitting alongside Billy, with Daniela on the other side of him, while opposite them were Juliet and Lorna. Somewhere under the blanket between her and Billy, Zoë felt the presence of the dog, and he provided welcome warmth to her legs as the horses trotted down to the old town, sleigh bells ringing, the sound of their hooves echoing through the streets, occasionally muffled by the snow as they crossed bits the snowploughs hadn't reached.

The old town was unmistakably Austrian, most of the buildings either made of wood or clad with wood. Although they weren't technically in the Tyrol, Billy assured them that the architecture was definitely Tyrolean. He explained that the Tyrol started only a few kilometres away from where they were. Indeed, Germany wasn't far to the north, with Italy just the other side of the big range of mountains to the south. Little wonder, then, that the menu tonight had been international.

The central area was a pedestrian zone, and here the snow was still thick on the ground. Hotels, bars and restaurants provided occasional patches of light as they glided past, and illuminated Christmas decorations hung across the road. The Christmas trees at the side of the road were now all lit up, and the whole place had a decidedly festive air to it. In many of the windows were candles and wonderful arrangements of greenery and pine cones, and a massive Christmas tree stood at the end of the street, with a glittering star at its top. The whole place had a magical feel to it and Zoë could imagine little Bella's eyes sparkling with wonder. She smiled to herself. It promised to be a fun week. After all, there was nothing better than seeing Christmas through the eyes of a child.

There were few, if any, street lights, and for much of the time the driver navigated by starlight. They came across odd groups of people walking along the snow-covered street, the dry snow crunching, almost squeaking, underneath their feet in the freezing temperature. It didn't take long to reach the other end of what was a very small town, and then the sledges returned to the hotel in a broad loop via a track through the snow-covered fields. The only sounds now were the muffled crunch of the horses' hooves in the snow and the gentle jingling of their decorative bells. The passengers could all see their own breath in the freezing air, and when they got back, they discovered that Martin's moustache was heavy with icicles. In spite of the blanket and the warm Labrador, Zoë herself was almost shivering with cold, and she made a mental note to put on an extra layer when she went skiing next morning.

Back at the hotel, Mandy and Bella retired to bed, while the rest of them headed for the bar to thaw out. Billy – ever the perfect host – offered them Glühwein and, although she was tempted, Zoë chose a glass of hot milk and honey instead. This did not go unnoticed.

'Shame on you, Zo. It's barely half past ten and you're drinking warm milk.' Lorna's voice was gently mocking. 'You'll be turning up in your dressing gown, curlers and slippers next. Come on, live a little. You're only thirty.'

'Thirty-two, but who's counting?'

As she said it, Zoë's eyes flicked across to Grant. She had been a full year younger this time last year when Grant had informed her he was leaving her for another woman. She dropped her eyes and snorted silently into her hot milk. She hadn't exchanged a single word with him since acknowledging his arrival, and she felt relieved. Over the months since the break-up, she had passed through an angry phase, a bitterly sad phase, then another angry one, followed by a more introspective stage when she had questioned whether she, too, bore some responsibility for his decision to leave. Could she have done more? *Should* she have done more? Lately, this had subsided into simple regret, but it was an ever-present nagging ache. Hopefully this holiday would be the cure she needed, allowing her to finally lay the memory of their time together to rest.

Her thoughts were interrupted by the sound of Daniela's voice.

'I'm surprised. You don't look thirty-two, Zoë.'

Zoë looked up and flashed her a smile.

'Thanks, Daniela. That does wonders for my self-confidence.'

The next voice belonged to her ex.

'She's right, you know, Zo. You look great.'

There was silence in the room as everybody — Zoë included — looked across at Grant. She could almost feel the anticipation as her friends waited with bated breath for her response. She took her time about it, wondering what, if anything, to say in reply. Finally she decided that to say nothing would risk poisoning what had been a lovely evening for everybody, so she limited herself to the bare minimum.

'I've been telling you for years to get your eyes tested, Grant.'

She decided against saying any more, but she was surprised to see what he did next. He reached into his trouser pocket and pulled out a slim leather case. From it he produced a pair of reading glasses, and set them on his nose.

'And I took your advice, Zo. So, what do you think? The absent-minded professor or what?'

'I think they make you look rather distinguished.' Lorna sounded quite impressed, but after the amount she had drunk today, her judgement wasn't to be trusted.

In fact, in a funny way, Zoë thought, the glasses didn't look out of place on him. For the first time today she allowed herself to subject him to close scrutiny. He was still tall and good-looking – his light brown hair now cut much shorter than before, but it still suited him. Like herself, it looked as though he had been working out and, if anything, he looked better than the last time she had seen him. Glasses or no glasses, he was still a handsome man. She steadfastly refused to allow even the slightest frisson of regret – or attraction – to run through her, but it wasn't easy.

Everybody was still looking at her, waiting for her answer, so she swallowed the rest of her milk and stood up, fortunately managing to avoid tripping over the dog as she did so.

'As long as they do the job, it doesn't matter what they look like.'

With that, she decided it was best not to say anything more to him tonight. She had acknowledged his existence, and she had been grown up enough to talk to him in civil tones, hadn't even considered picking up a chair and smacking him with it, in spite of the way he had treated her, but enough was enough. Setting down her empty glass, she went across to Billy and Daniela and gave them both a warm smile and a hug.

'Thank you most sincerely for inviting me here to this wonderful place. I know it's going to be a fabulous Christmas and I'm going to do my best to enjoy every minute of it.'

They both smiled back at her as Billy answered.

'I hope you do. As I said, I've got to pop down to Salzburg tomorrow, otherwise I'd come skiing with you. The day after, hopefully.'

'Definitely.'

She turned back towards the others – Grant included – and gave them a little wave.

'Goodnight, everybody. See you in the morning.' She let her smile broaden. 'And tomorrow, we're going skiing! I've been dreaming of this for months.'

Back in her room, she pulled out her laptop and typed a few notes – *married, owner of hotel, speaks German, Austrian heritage* – just to remind her. However, the more she got to know Billy, and particularly after what he had said about *HC* magazine, she felt very dubious whether the article would ever be written. One thing was for sure – there was no way she was going to betray his trust, even if she had a feeling her refusal to obey her boss's orders might end up costing her her job.

Chapter 6

Zoë woke up after a wonderful night's sleep wrapped in her blissfully warm duvet and stretched luxuriously. Although she had only used half of the massive bed, she had ended up rolled snugly into the whole king-size duvet as though it was a cocoon. For a moment she remembered how often Grant had complained at her habit of hogging the covers, but she immediately suppressed the memory, deciding that the thought of Grant and her bed in the same breath was not welcome. Even so, she soon found herself thinking back to what she had seen of him so far, and she had to admit – albeit grudgingly – that her first impression had been remarkably positive. He was looking good, had behaved himself impeccably, and hadn't drunk too much. In fact, if she didn't know him of old, she would have been pleasantly impressed by him. But of course, just as underneath Billy's veneer of sophistication there was still the same timid, nerdy guy from number 23, so she felt sure the real womanising, deceitful, callous Grant was no doubt lying below the surface of this new grown-up incarnation.

Her phone told her it was seven thirty, so she got up, went across to the window and opened the curtains.

To her delight, the first rays of early-morning sunshine came flooding in. It was wonderfully warm in her room, no doubt due to the insulating effect of having two sets of windows – an inner pair and an outer pair – with a gap in between. Although familiar with double-glazing, this was the first time she had come across anything so radical as having two complete sets of windows, but there was no doubting their thermal efficiency. In just her pyjamas and bare feet, she was as warm as toast, while outside on the balcony she could see long icicles hanging like stalactites from the wooden handrail. Beyond that, everything was white.

As predicted, it had snowed in the night. The balcony itself was covered with three or four inches of perfect virginal snow, and a gentle breeze blew individual snow-flakes around in the sub-zero air. As she looked out, a snowflake the size of a pea landed on the glass right in front of her and she could clearly see the perfect symmetry of its crystalline design before it gradually melted away into an amorphous droplet. It was a stunning way to start the day.

Breakfast was already laid out in the dining room, and Zoë was mildly surprised to find that she was not the first person in there, although it was still early. Juliet had beaten her to it and was sitting at a table by the window, a plate of smoked ham and cheese in front of her. Beyond her, standing by a table groaning with food, was a waitress wearing the trademark green and white uniform. She also had a pair of reindeer antlers on her head and Zoë smiled at her across the room as she walked over to Juliet.

'Hi, Jules. Mind if I join you?'

'Please do. Sleep well?'

'Like a log. I didn't hear a single thing all night.' She allowed herself a moment of nostalgia. 'The soundproofing must be very good – I didn't even hear Grant's snoring from along the corridor. What about you?'

'Lovely. The rooms are gorgeous, aren't they? What a place! So… are we going skiing this morning?'

'Definitely.'

Zoë went across to the food table and helped herself to a bowl of fruit salad containing everything from cherries and blueberries to star fruit and prunes, and a wonderful-smelling warm bread roll with a little pot of honey. Prompted by the waitress, she opted for hot chocolate, and this arrived at her table shortly after she had sat down.

As the waitress retired, Juliet looked across the table at Zoë with a quizzical expression on her face.

'So, how did your first sight of Grant go?'

'A lot better than I feared. And thank God he's here on his own. I was dreading being cooped up with his woman. But seeing him last night, I think he was as nervous as I was.'

'He deserved to be!' Juliet still showed no signs of forgiving Grant for his treatment of Zoë.

'Damn right, but at least I feel pretty sure we're going to be able to co-exist for a week or so without causing a scene. It's time I put the past behind me and made a fresh start. I'm going to enjoy every day as it comes, and hopefully by the time we leave I'll be back to how I used to be. I'm going to do my very best to enjoy this holiday I've been dreaming of for so long.'

'Me too. So how about Billy, then?' There was a tone of wonder in Juliet's voice.

'I know. Talk about a different man! I genuinely didn't recognise him at first.'

'He's looking really good, isn't he? And Daniela's gorgeous.' Juliet sounded seriously impressed. She caught Zoë's eye. 'Pity he's married, eh, Zo?'

Zoë gave her a stern look. 'Like I said, I'm not interested in finding myself a man, and neither are you from what you told me. Besides, he *is* married and you and I aren't like Grant. I wish Billy and Daniela well.'

'Me too.'

—

Zoë and Juliet, well wrapped up, and equipped with their new ski passes, met in the hotel lobby at eight thirty and crunched through the fresh snow along the icy drive to the ski shop. It was very slippery underfoot and Zoë was mildly surprised that she managed to get there without falling flat on her face. Ever since childhood she had had a tendency to be a bit accident-prone, as her former housemates knew only too well. The occasion when she had tripped in the lounge and showered Juliet and Lorna with chicken tikka masala would never be forgotten. However, this morning there was no curry in the vicinity, and her feet and her balance were up to the task.

The air was still absolutely freezing and both of them were glad of their thick clothing. Zoë even pulled up her scarf to cover her cheeks and nose until she got used to the cold. In the ski shop, they found they were expected, and she was impressed – if unsurprised – to find herself kitted out with top-of-the-range skis and boots completely free of charge. Billy's generosity clearly knew no bounds.

The guy who fitted them with their skis and boots also gave them pocket-sized maps of the pistes and pointed them in the direction of the main chairlift. This was barely a hundred yards along the road, and when they got there, Zoë was delighted to find there was virtually no queue. No queue down here boded well for a crowd-free day on the slopes.

They took their seats on the fast four-seater lift, which whisked them up the mountain. The sun had yet to get round to here and it was still very cold, gliding along a few metres above the snow-covered treetops below. Zoë pulled her woolly hat right down to her eyes and both of them hunched into their clothing. She was very glad when the lift reached the top and they could get moving again.

Up here, they found themselves on a gently sloping plateau with a fine chalet-style restaurant with a wide sun terrace to one side and more lifts away to the right of them at the bottom of the slope. Best of all, by now the sun had reached the lower slopes, so they checked their bindings, pulled down their goggles and set off – slowly at first – down towards the sunshine.

They both had a wonderful morning. Juliet was pretty good on skis and they skied together for several hours, gradually working their way across the mountainside and down a few of the more difficult runs. Juliet fell over a few times, but Zoë was pleased – and relieved – to manage the whole morning without incident. Clearly she still remem- bered how to do it. In fact, as the morning progressed, she felt increasingly secure on her skis and was able to enjoy the scenery as well as the experience. Although they weren't the only people on the pistes by any means, they were able to ski at their own pace without being held up or, more importantly, dive-bombed by lunatics flying down the slopes out of control. Zoë still preferred to ski without a helmet, although more and more people were taking to them, but here at least it looked as though it shouldn't be too dangerous. The other surprise was that they heard very few English voices. It looked as though Bad Bergstein was a resort mainly frequented by Austrians. Zoë rather liked the idea of being among the locals.

She eyed the fresh snow amidst the pine trees away from the pistes longingly, but decided to wait until she had a local – maybe Billy – to show her the way. Although very competent, Juliet said she preferred to stay on the beaten runs, and that suited Zoë fine on her first outing for more than two years. By eleven o'clock they had both definitely warmed up and were in need of refreshment, so they headed back to the restaurant by the top of the first lift – Gasthof zum Wilden Hirsch.

Zoë seemed to remember that *Hirsch* meant deer, and her hunch was confirmed as they clomped in through the door in their ski boots and then past the thick thermal blanket screen hanging behind it. Sure enough, the first thing they saw inside was a massive stuffed stag's head sporting a magnificent set of antlers – definitely not plastic, these – hanging on the wall in front of them. The second thing they saw was a long counter displaying all manner of delicious-looking food. It was spotlessly clean and there was even a man with a mop, wiping up the meltwater by the door where ski boots had brought in snow and ice. The whole room was hung with Christmas decorations and she could hear 'Jingle Bells' playing on the PA system. On the far side of the crowded room, French windows led out onto the even more crowded terrace, now bathed in sunlight.

They went out to see if they could find a table, and it was looking a forlorn hope until they spotted Grant sitting with Fergus. Zoë stopped dead, but then, after a brief internal debate, collected herself and led Juliet across to them.

'Good morning, gentlemen. What are you doing? Skiing or snowboarding?'

Grant appeared uncharacteristically tongue-tied as Fergus answered for both of them.

'Boarding. We're both totally hooked on it.'

Zoë was really surprised. Somehow she had assumed that quiet, reserved, rather formal Fergus would have looked down his nose at a Johnny-come-lately sport like snowboarding. Not at all. He was even wearing a fleece emblazoned with the names of famous boarders. Wonders never ceased.

'Imogen decided not to join you?'

Fergus shook his head.

'I've just been telling Grant. She's more of a sit-in-the-bar-and-watch-it-happen sort of winter sports girl.'

'She doesn't know what she's missing.'

'You two going to join us for a coffee?' Grant finally found his voice and indicated the empty bench opposite him. 'I promise I'll try not to make you spill it this time, Zo.'

Juliet and Zoë exchanged glances and then sat down as invited. As they did so, Grant jumped to his feet.

'What's it going to be? Your usual cappuccino and a bottle of mineral water, Zo? What about you, Jules?'

'The same, please, but we're paying.'

But Grant disappeared towards the bar before either of them could stop him. After he had left, Fergus surprised Zoë yet again.

'He knows you so well, doesn't he? Is it a bit weird for you to be here at the same time as your ex?'

Of course Imogen must have filled him in on her background by now, but this was just about the first personal thing he had said to Zoë. He was looking and sounding far more relaxed and communicative than last night. Whether this was the influence of the fresh mountain air or because he had got away from the controlling presence of his wife was difficult to assess. Zoë answered frankly.

'It feels a bit strange, although, to be honest, Fergus, I'm finding it easier than I expected.'

'As long as he continues to behave himself.' Juliet's tone made it clear that she hadn't forgiven Grant yet. Nor, indeed, had Zoë, but she really was finding being with him far less stressful than she had feared – at least so far. She decided to change the subject.

'And what about you and Imogen, Fergus? All going well?'

For a moment she distinctly saw him hesitate, but then he nodded.

'It's all good. This is the first real holiday we've had since getting married, and we've both been dreaming about it for months.'

This came as a real surprise to Zoë. She would have imagined that this well-heeled pair would have been off on numerous trips to glamorous destinations, but maybe his job was more demanding on his time than she had thought. Or was there more to it than met the eye?

'We've both been dreaming about it too.' This time, Juliet's tone was bright. 'Isn't Billy an absolute star?'

'He's amazingly generous.' Fergus nodded into his beer. 'I've met a lot of stinking-rich people over the years and you'd be amazed how mean many of them can be.'

'I suppose that's how to get rich and stay rich. Once you've got it, don't give it away. Mind you, Billy must be worth a good few millions, so a few thou here or there is probably small change to him.'

Fergus shook his head.

'Not millions, Juliet. Billy's worth *billions*.' Seeing the expressions on their faces, he elaborated. 'Our bank does a lot of business with WF Computer Systems. Without giving away any confidential secrets, you can take it from me he's got enough money to buy half of Austria – if he hasn't already done so.'

'Wow.' Zoë didn't know what to say. She mentally added this fact to the list for an article on the *reclusive* Mr Fischer. If it ever happened.

'What are you wowing about?' Grant reappeared with a tray.

'Billy. Fergus has been telling us just how amazingly wealthy he must be.'

'Billy's done very well for himself.'

Grant unloaded the coffees and little bottles of water. He also set a plate on the table containing four slices of what he told them was called *Sachertorte* – chocolate cake layered with apricot jam and covered in dark chocolate icing.

'It's pretty damn cold, so we all need a few extra calories.'

'A few? One slice of this probably contains enough calories to keep a family of four going for a week!'

Zoë complained, but she didn't refuse her slice and it was predictably excellent.

As they ate the cake and drank their drinks, the four of them chatted and Zoë was relieved to find that the relative ease with which she had been able to talk to Grant yesterday still continued today. In fact, to an onlooker, it would have sounded like a perfectly normal conversation. Of course, needless to say, it only sounded normal because their former relationship and its abrupt ending were not discussed.

It was really remarkably warm in the sunshine and Zoë was glad she had protected her face with sun cream before leaving the hotel. She knew all too well how strong the sun could be at altitude and she had no desire to get burnt. She had removed her ski goggles, but she now needed her sunglasses as the light reflecting on the snow was blinding. The views from up here were amazing, and they all took some photos. Zoë even found herself being photographed by, and with, Grant, but she gritted her teeth and put up with it.

Below them, the ski slopes ran down towards the town, and beyond that, her eyes could follow the valley all the way into the distance, almost as far as Salzburg itself – although that was a bit further around the corner. It was a spectacular view, particularly with the massive mountains rising up behind them, their glistening snow-covered peaks contrasting with the intense cerulean blue of the cloudless sky. Grant or no Grant, Zoë felt good.

When she and Juliet left the restaurant to resume their progress across the slopes, the two men came out with them and headed off on their snowboards. Neither of them suggested making a foursome of it, and that suited Zoë just fine.

—

Fortified by their slices of *Sachertorte*, Zoë and Juliet chose to stay out over lunchtime, and it was almost four o'clock when they finally called it a day and set off back down the hill to home. As the hotel website had predicted, they were able to ski right down to the hotel itself. Since they had left their normal shoes back at the ski shop, they headed back there and dumped their skis and boots ready for the next morning. As they walked back up the snowy drive to the hotel, enjoying the feel of getting away from the rigidity of their ski boots, Zoë massaged her thighs.

'I'm glad I've been spending a bit of time in the gym – I ache enough as it is. I wonder how Martin and Bella are getting on.'

Martin and Bella, along with Mandy, were waiting for them back in their private lounge. Sitting with them were Imogen and Lorna, with a half-empty bottle of champagne on the table between them. Lorna offered them a glass as they walked in, but Zoë shook her head.

'Thanks, Lorn, but I need to go and have a long, hot bath. I'm clearly not as fit as I thought I was.' She transferred her attention to Mandy's family. 'So, Bella, how did your first day's skiing go?'

'It was fun, but the snow's cold when you fall on it.'

'Did you fall over a lot?'

The little girl nodded, looking a bit uncertain, so Zoë decided to give her a bit of positive reinforcement.

'That's good. Remember, you've got to fall over a thousand times before you become a real skier. At least that's what they told me when I was learning – and I did a lot of falling over.'

Bella looked relieved and her father patted her head as he groaned theatrically.

'I'm sure Bella fell over fewer times than I did. And I've got further to fall.'

Zoë transferred her attention to Imogen.

'We saw Fergus on his snowboard. He's really good. You should try it, Imogen. I bet you'd enjoy it.'

She saw Imogen shudder at the thought.

'Rather him than me. I've had a lovely day. I've been for a walk into town and done a bit of shopping, I've read my book, and I've eaten far too much. That's my idea of a really excellent day, and it certainly beats working.'

'What are you doing these days, Imogen?'

Zoë knew she had studied social science, but had no idea what sort of career she had chosen.

'I've got a boutique in Richmond, right in the centre – top-of-the-range designer fashion. I've always wanted to be my own boss, and this has turned out to be the best decision I ever made.'

'Apart from marrying Fergus.' Mandy was quick to point out her omission. For a fraction of a second, Zoë spotted the same slight hesitation she had noted in Fergus, before Imogen nodded her head.

'Yes, of course, apart from Fergus.'

Maybe sensing some slight tension in the air, Mandy caught Zoë's eye.

'Why don't you and Jules stay for a cup of tea and a piece of cake before going off to have your baths? The food's delicious here.'

Zoë shook her head.

'I know it is, but I must be strong. I've already had a massive great slab of cake today and I'm sure dinner will be wonderful, so I'll be a good girl and give tea a miss. See you guys later.'

Chapter 7

After her bath – during which she very nearly drifted off to sleep – Zoë decided to dress up a bit for dinner. Not, she told herself firmly, that this was for Grant's sake. Rather, it was as a gesture to Billy, whose wonderful hotel deserved a bit of effort on her part. It took her a while – she had got out of the habit of wearing very smart clothes or using lipstick – but the end result looked fairly reasonable when she studied herself in the mirror. It was so warm in the hotel, she could easily have worn a summer frock if she had brought one, but instead she chose one of the two smart dresses she had packed, along with her only pair of heels. The dress was far from being what Imogen had described as top-of-the-range-designer fashion, but it had been fairly expensive – at least by Zoë's standards – and she knew she looked pretty good in it.

She had just about finished when there was a light tap on the door. She went over and opened it, to be greeted by an effusive Labrador and his master. As she crouched down to pet the dog before he could jump up and ladder her tights, she heard Billy's voice, sounding quite awestruck.

'Wow, Zoë, you look like a million dollars.'

Remembering what Fergus had said earlier about Billy's billionaire status, Zoë reflected that a million dollars would probably fall into the category of small change as far as her host was concerned. However, she avoided any mention of money as she straightened up again and smiled at him.

'Thanks, Billy. I'm glad you think so. I thought I'd dress up a bit for your sake.'

'For my sake?'

For a moment she caught a glimpse of the old, timid Billy, staring blankly at her with an awkward look on his face. She reminded herself she was talking to a married man, so to avoid any misunderstandings, she hastened to explain.

'I mean for the sake of this wonderful hotel. It's all so smart and perfect. It feels wrong to be wandering around in just jeans and a jumper somehow.'

As she spoke, she took a closer look at him and saw that this was exactly what he was wearing – jeans and another lovely soft V-neck jumper – this time a chestnut-brown colour that matched his hair. She gave him a smile.

'Naturally you can wear whatever you like, Billy, but I thought I'd make a bit of an effort. Do you realise, I've even put on a bit of lippy? This is the first time I've dressed up for a year now.'

She crouched back down again to scratch the Labrador's tummy as he rolled about on his back, grunting to himself, tail wagging happily.

'It's been a tough year for you, hasn't it?'

Billy's tone was so caring, so compassionate, that for a moment Zoë felt a stinging in the corners of her eyes as the emotional baggage she had been carrying with her threatened to spill out. She took a couple of deep, calming breaths before replying.

'It has been tough, Billy. It's very sweet of you to mention it, but I'm doing fine now.'

'I'm glad to hear you sounding so strong. When I heard about your break-up, I was afraid you might have been badly scarred as a result.'

Zoë stood back up again and touched his arm, enjoying seeing him blush. Then, regretting making fun of such a nice guy, she released him.

'Thanks, Billy. I'm doing a lot better now – and this holiday of yours is exactly what I needed.'

'Good, I'm glad. And just remember, if there's anything I can do, anything you need, please tell me. You know I've always liked you.'

Zoë almost gave him a kiss for being so sweet, but she restrained herself for fear that he might explode with embarrassment, and just gave his forearm another little squeeze.

'Thanks, Billy. You're a sweetie. And I've always liked you too.' And she had, but she really had known so little about him back in the scruffy surroundings of number 23.

There was a slight pause before he spoke again.

'Anyway, Zoë, the reason I knocked on your door was to ask if you felt like coming skiing with Daniela and me tomorrow. I thought I'd ask you quietly first as I imagine you'd prefer not to ski with Grant after everything that's happened. Maybe Juliet might like to come too? I believe you were with her today – she's quite good, isn't she?'

'Yes indeed, to everything. And I don't even care if Grant comes too. I'm finding dealing with him a lot easier than I thought it was going to be. I'd love to come skiing with you and Daniela, and yes, Juliet's pretty good. She doesn't like the deep stuff and prefers to stay on the pistes, though.'

'Daniela, too. Perhaps one day this week, if you fancy it, you and I could have a go at the powder – maybe with Grant and Fergus if you really don't mind. The conditions at the moment are excellent off piste, with more snow forecast tomorrow or the day after – so if you're up for it, I know the area pretty well by now and I'd love to show you round. There are a few spots to avoid because of the risk of avalanche, but I know those by now and I'll make sure we stay safe.'

'It's a date. Fabulous, Billy. So, tomorrow us two with Daniela and Juliet on piste, then one day you and I hit the powder snow.' It sounded wonderful. Whether it would be so wonderful if Grant came along was another matter, but she would cross that bridge when she came to it.

As they walked into the lounge, Zoë noticed a few raised eyebrows, notably on Imogen and Lorna's faces. Predictably, Lorna was the first to comment.

'Bloody hell, Zoë, that's not fair. Who said you could dress up like the Queen of Sheba this evening while the rest of us look like a bunch of bums?'

Beyond her, standing in the corner alongside Fergus, Zoë spotted Grant, his eyes trained on her and an expression on his face with which she had been unfamiliar over the past few years. Unless she was very much mistaken, the expression was desire. Unbidden, she felt a flush spread to her face and hastily dropped her eyes to the dog, who had noticed that she was wearing a new pair of shoes. She bent down and did her best to dissuade him from chewing them. They were the only smart shoes she had brought – and they hadn't been cheap.

'Arnie, get off. Go and play with somebody else.' She glanced across to where Mandy and her family were sitting. 'Bella, why don't you come and play with the doggy?'

To her relief, the little girl came running across, and soon she and the pup were happily playing together, and Zoë's shoes – at least for now – were safe from molestation.

As Zoë stood up again, she felt herself under observation once more, this time by Imogen. As their eyes met, Imogen passed judgement on Zoë's appearance.

'You look lovely, Zoë. Tell me, where did you get that super little dress?'

There was no point in trying to pretend. Zoë felt quite sure that Imogen's eagle eye had already worked out its provenance and probably its price to the nearest 99p. She gave a rueful smile.

'It's nothing special, Imogen. Certainly not the sort of stuff *you* sell – or wear. I bought it in the sales a couple of years ago. At least it still fits.'

'It's quite charming.'

'Thank you.'

'I think it looks great.' It was Fergus.

Zoë looked at him in surprise. Apart from their conversation up on the slopes this morning, Fergus had hardly spoken a word to her, and certainly not in the presence of his wife. She got the distinct impression that the look Imogen shot him was one of disapproval. Zoë herself gave him a big smile.

'Well, thanks, Fergus. And you're looking as smart as usual.' Although, thankfully, he had abandoned his suit tonight and was wearing a crisp white shirt with the collar open. Just then, she heard another voice.

'And I think you look terrific too.'

Zoë's eyes flicked across to acknowledge Grant's comment, but she made no response. Instead, she walked over to the bar and helped herself to a bottle of beer. As she took a sip, she was joined by Juliet, who had also dressed up and was looking very elegant. A few seconds later, Daniela appeared and eclipsed them both – at least in Zoë's eyes. She was wearing a gorgeous pale pink dress that screamed class and expense. Even a fashion ingénue like Zoë could see that. What was nice, however, was how natural she looked, in spite of being dressed like a Hollywood starlet. It was also lovely to see her go up to her husband and give him a little kiss on the cheek.

A twinge of envy at their happiness shot through Zoë's body and she was unable to prevent her eyes from flicking, momentarily, back towards Grant. Taking a firm grip of her emotions, she tore her attention away from him and swallowed a big mouthful of beer. Alas, in so doing, she made the mistake of allowing the bottle to escape her lips, and a splash of foam shot up her nose and set her off in a coughing fit.

'You all right, Zo?' Juliet handed her a handful of servicttes. 'Here, wipe yourself off. You'll ruin that lovely dress.'

It was a minute or so before Zoë was able to draw breath properly, and she could still feel her cheeks burning with embarrassment. Beside her she could sense Juliet shaking with barely contained laughter as she heard Lorna's voice.

'Clumsy Lumsey's alive and well. Some things never change, folks.'

As Zoë wiped her eyes and then her face with more of the abundant supply of serviettes, she heard Billy explain to his wife, 'Zoë had a bit of a reputation at university for being clumsy. Her name's Lumsley, but it soon became Clumsy Lumsey. I think it's rather endearing.'

Zoë managed to regain the power of speech.

'That's easy for you to say. You're not the one with a nose full of beer.'

Billy then changed the subject and gave Zoë time to recover.

'Anyway, tonight, rather than having dinner here in the hotel, I've booked a table in a restaurant in the old town. How does that sound?'

That sounded wonderful – although Zoë and Juliet wisely hurried back to their rooms before going out to change into warmer clothes and more suitable shoes. They set off for the short walk to the restaurant at just after seven. Juliet took a firm hold of Zoë's arm as they made their way through the snowy streets, and Zoë was grateful. It would be the height of irony if she were to fall and break her leg in the town, rather than out on the mountainside. It was very quiet, and she realised what it was she had been missing. Compared to London, there was virtually no traffic – apart from an occasional car or the local bus – and the silence was almost disconcerting.

The restaurant was very much the opposite. As they came in from the relative peace and quiet and threaded their way through the already crowded room to the table reserved for them, the volume of noise was a real assault on the ears. Apart from the chatter of sixty or seventy guests, there was an accordion player – dressed in leather shorts and jaunty hat with a feather in it – playing some sort of traditional drinking song, and a number of people were singing along to the music. The place was hung with garlands and baubles but still had a very Austrian feel, and it looked as though almost all the guests were Austrian. Zoë shot a glance across at Juliet and saw her smile back.

'I suppose we should be grateful it isn't a full oompah band.'

'Don't speak too soon. There might be one waiting in the wings.'

No doubt as a result of a good bit of forethought and planning on Billy's part, their table was tucked in the far corner, well away from the music. Zoë made sure she sat at the opposite end of the table from Grant, sandwiched between Juliet and an excited Bella, who was perched on a couple of cushions. As she sat down, Zoë leant towards the little girl.

'Have you ever been to a place like this before?'

Bella shook her head. 'No, but it's fun, isn't it?'

Zoë smiled. The little girl's excitement was infectious, and she felt a wave of happiness – just about the first real happiness for a year – sweep over her. From where she was sitting, she couldn't see Grant, and he might just as well not have existed. She was here in this magnificent mountain resort with a bunch of old friends, and it felt good to be alive. On impulse, she caught hold of Bella by the shoulders and gave her a hug and a kiss. Then she turned to Juliet and did the same. As she did so, she saw Juliet's eyes twinkle.

'What was that for, Zo?'

'Just for being a good friend. I'm so glad I'm here, we're here – in fact, I'm glad we're *all* here.'

'All…?'

'Well, almost all.'

She needed very little persuading to join most of the others in ordering a large beer. She was not, however, expecting what then arrived at the table. A burly waitress in traditional costume arrived with half a dozen huge glass mugs of beer in her powerful hands and distributed them around the table. Zoë shot a look across the table at Daniela.

'Are these pints?'

Daniela grinned and shook her head.

'No, litres.' She glanced sideways towards Billy. 'How much is a litre in your measurements?'

'The best part of two pints.'

Once she had got over her shock, Zoë picked up the heavy glass, leant forward and dipped her mouth into the frothy beer. It tasted great, even if it gave her a white moustache. Seconds later she was surprised, and impressed, to hear Grant's voice from the end of the table.

'I'd like to propose a toast to Billy for his tremendous generosity. I'm sure we're all very, very grateful for your invitation. Bad Bergstein's a super place, the hotel's amazing, this restaurant's great, and you've been brilliant. Here's to you, Billy.'

'To Billy!'

Everybody echoed Grant's words as they clinked the heavy mugs against each other. As she did so, Zoë couldn't help feeling astonished that her ex-boyfriend had behaved so politely – almost like a real grown-up. Maybe he had matured over the past year. It was certainly about time.

She and Juliet allowed themselves to be persuaded to try that most quintessential of Austrian dishes – a Wiener Schnitzel. When they arrived, they were so huge, Zoë genuinely feared she wouldn't be able to finish it, but she surprised herself. The meat inside the fried breadcrumbs was thin and the whole thing was remarkably light, the accompaniment just a few potatoes and a mixed salad. She had little difficulty in clearing her plate.

'There's nothing like a day's skiing to give you an appetite, eh, Zo?' Juliet too had polished off her Schnitzel.

After quenching her thirst with the excellent beer, Zoë nodded in agreement. Setting down the heavy glass, she wiped away her beer moustache and grinned at her friend.

'And tomorrow we get to do it all again.'

The inevitable happened on the way home. Whether it was the litre of beer she had drunk or just Zoë's natural clumsiness, as they made their way back up the road towards home, she slipped on an icy patch and fell sideways into one of the huge piles of snow left by the passage of the snowplough. As she fell, she pulled Juliet down with her and the two of them ended up face-first in the snow. She heard a little cheer go up and then strong hands caught her under the arms and pulled her clear. As she straightened up, wiping freezing snow from her face, she found that her saviour had been none other than Grant, and he was still gripping her shoulders to steady her. She took an unsteady step backwards out of his reach and caught hold of Juliet again – freshly rescued from the snow by Fergus and Martin – feeling rather pleased that there weren't any street lights round her to reveal her glowing cheeks.

'Thank you, Grant.' She remembered her manners.

'You all right, Zo?' He sounded genuinely concerned for her well-being.

'I'm fine, thanks. Just embarrassed.' Whether the embarrassment was as a result of her fall or being picked up by him wasn't clear to her at this stage. She could still feel the touch of his hands on her body and she wasn't totally sure how to interpret the sensation.

'It's a wonder you can stay upright on skis, Zo.' Lorna was grinning at her in the starlight.

'I was thinking the same thing.' Juliet was grinning as well, in spite of her excursion into the white stuff. 'Your balance can't be that bad after all, Zo.'

'Keep telling yourself that, Jules. We've still got a hundred yards to go. You might find yourself on your face in the snow again.'

'Here, Zoë, let me give you a hand.' Lorna came over and took hold of her arm. 'I've got this side of you and, Jules, if you hang onto the other side of Zoë, the three of us should be solid as a rock.'

Zoë gripped the two girls and they set off again. Lorna was right. Between them, they managed to return to the hotel without further incident. When they got back upstairs, Zoë thanked Lorna and apologised profusely to Juliet. She almost repeated her thanks to Grant for helping her out of the snow, but decided against it.

Daniela disappeared along the corridor to Billy's suite, and a few seconds later, the Labrador came charging down to see them all. After greeting his master, he headed straight for Zoë. This time she was wearing trousers over her tights, so she let him stand up on his hind legs as she caught hold of his paws and gave them a little shake.

'And good evening to you too, sir. You missed a lovely meal.'

'Arnie, get down! I've told you about that. No jumping up, all right?'

Even Zoë could hear the lack of authority in Billy's tone. The dog looked totally unapologetic as he returned grudgingly to all fours and then did a tour of the room, getting petted from all sides. Finally satisfied that he had said hello to everybody, he came back over and parked himself right on top of Zoë's feet as usual – mercifully without attempting to tear her shoes apart this time. Wisely, Zoë caught hold of the arm of the sofa and gently lowered herself to a less vulnerable position.

'Beer, wine, champagne, Glühwein?'

Billy was still acting as the perfect host. The litre of beer she had drunk at the restaurant was more than enough alcohol for Zoë, so she settled for another hot milk and further ridicule from Lorna. She was feeling pleasantly sleepy by now, and it wasn't long before she and Juliet headed off to their rooms, with Billy's parting words ringing in their ears.

'Meet in the lobby at eight thirty. All right?'

Back in her room, Zoë wasted no time in getting ready for bed. Her thighs weren't aching too badly, but she felt exhausted after all the physical activity, the fresh air and two pints of beer. She was just buttoning up her pyjamas when there was a soft tap on the door. She padded across, opened it a few inches and peered out.

Standing there was Grant.

'What do you want, Grant?' She kept her voice low so as not to disturb the others, but also to keep a lid on her emotions.

She heard him clear his throat before speaking.

'I was wondering if you and I could have a talk, Zo.'

He sounded uncharacteristically insecure, but she wasn't buying it.

'What, now? With me in my pyjamas?'

'Um, not necessarily. Any time really.'

'Have we got anything to talk about, Grant? I don't think so. You did all the talking a year ago.'

She was pleased to hear her voice sounding firm, although inside she was in tumult. Finally, the moment she had been dreading had arrived – just the two of them together.

'I think I owe you an apology, Zo.'

'You *think* you owe me an apology?' Zoë felt the anger she had been trying so hard to suppress come bubbling up.

'I mean, I know I do. You see, Zo… I've been very, very stupid.'

'Well you got that right, at least. Now, I'm going to sleep, Grant. Just go away, will you?' And without giving him the chance to say anything else, she closed the door quietly, but firmly, in his face.

Chapter 8

When Zoë woke up next morning, she wasn't feeling as fresh as she might have done. In spite of her tiredness, it had taken her a considerable while to get to sleep the previous night, and the reason for that was all too obvious – Grant.

She checked her phone and saw that it was almost seven o'clock on Thursday 20th December, just five days away from Christmas. She lay there, snuggled under the duvet, thinking back over everything that had occupied her mind last night and throughout the preceding twelve months. It was hard to believe that less than a year ago she had still been happily in love with Grant and blissfully unaware of the bombshell he was about to deliver. It was an uncomfortable sort of anniversary to consider.

What had so exercised her brain overnight had been the realisation that he appeared to have matured over the past year and maybe still had feelings for her – or so it seemed. Had this been what he had wanted to talk about last night? Had he come to Austria in a bid to win her back, in spite of having broken her heart so callously?

And if he had come with that intention, how did she feel about it? Yes, he still looked good, he appeared more caring and considerate, and he showed signs of behaving like a grown-up at long last. But was this just an illusion, an act? And, whether it was or not, could she really even begin to consider forgiving him and letting him have the chance to make amends, to kick-start their relationship? Surely, if he had even the slightest idea of how truly awful these last twelve months had been for her, he couldn't possibly believe she would be prepared to welcome him back into her life. And was she just plain crackers to even begin to consider that possibility, after the way he had behaved?

It was with a heavy heart that she finally roused herself and went through to take a shower. Her visit to the bathroom did nothing to answer the conundrum, but it did, at least, wake her up to the fact that she had a full day's skiing ahead of her. A glance out of the window showed her that the predicted snow had yet to arrive and the morning sun was shining as brightly as the previous day. Her spirits began to lift once more.

As she came out of her room, she saw Juliet emerge from her own room, just a bit further along the corridor.

'Morning, Jules. Sleep well?'

'Like a top. What about you? You all right? You're looking a bit down in the mouth.'

As they walked down to the dining room, past the reception desk where Erika was already on duty, Zoë gave Juliet a brief summary of the exchange she had had with Grant. Juliet looked appalled.

'So do you think he's trying to get you to take him back, after everything that's happened?' Her tone was incredulous.

'I really don't know, but I think it might be what he's hoping.'

'You'd never do that, though, would you?' Juliet stopped outside the dining room door and caught Zoë by the arm. 'Would you?'

'No, of course not. Or at least, I don't think so… Oh Jules, I don't know. I feel like such a fool. How can I even begin to consider getting back together with somebody who treated me that way – even if he has changed?'

'You think he's changed?'

'I don't know…' Zoë knew she was sounding completely clueless. 'He's been looking and acting a good bit more grown-up, but mind you, this is the man who was having an affair with another woman right under my nose and I didn't notice anything. Besides, for all I know, he may still be with this other woman. Billy said he didn't mention her, but that proves nothing. He's good at hiding things.'

Juliet nodded her head in agreement. 'Just keep remembering that, Zo. If you want my opinion, I wouldn't trust him an inch. As far as I'm concerned, it's all an act designed to get you back into his bed, if not his life.'

Zoë nodded ruefully. Juliet was making a lot of sense.

Inside the dining room, they noticed Fergus and Grant sitting together by the window. Studiously ignoring Grant, Zoë waved to Fergus before helping herself to fruit salad and yoghurt. Today she decided she needed a strong coffee to go with her bread and honey, and she even allowed herself to be persuaded by the waitress to have a ham omelette as extra fortification before braving the sub-zero temperatures outside.

She and Juliet chose to sit at the furthest table from Grant. Zoë saw surprise and even hurt on Fergus's face as they did so, and resolved to explain to him later that she had just been trying to maintain decent boundaries between herself and her ex – not him.

They had only been sitting there for a few minutes when the door opened and Lorna appeared, dressed in outdoor clothes. She ordered a large black coffee and came over to join the two of them.

'Morning, girls. You off skiing again?'

'That's right. And you, Lorn, are you going out?' Zoë could hear the incredulity in her own voice.

Lorna grinned and nodded. 'Don't look so shocked. I do venture out from time to time, you know. Today I'm going down to Salzburg on the train with Imogen, and maybe Mandy. After you two lightweights had gone off to bed last night, Billy suggested going to a concert there this evening, so we girls thought we'd make a day of it.'

'That sounds exciting. What sort of concert?'

'Classical, and in a gorgeous place called the Mirabell Palace. Guess whose music, bearing in mind where we are?'

It wasn't too hard to guess. Salzburg had been the birthplace of one of the greatest composers of all time.

'Wolfgang Amadeus Mozart by any chance? How wonderful.'

Zoë wasn't really a classical music buff, but the idea of a Christmas concert in a magnificent Austrian palace had distinct appeal. The day was looking up.

–

Zoë and Juliet met Billy and Daniela in the lobby at eight thirty as arranged. Outside, it was fractionally warmer than the previous day, but still cold enough to have Zoë burrowing her nose into her scarf and tugging her hat down until the two almost touched and she was squinting out through a narrow slit. There were a few more people around today, as Christmas approached, but even so, they barely had to queue more than two minutes for the lift. As they travelled up, doing their best to stay warm, the four of them chatted and Billy told them more about the concert that evening.

'Tonight they're doing a series of Mozart violin sonatas. Even if you aren't that keen on classical music, I guarantee you'll love the setting – a historic old palace, with marble floors and more gold leaf on the walls than paint. It's not a long show. It starts early – at five o'clock – and we should be out before six thirty. That way little Bella can come too and she won't be too tired. I thought we could leave here at, say, three, and I'll get the driver to give us a quick tour of the city before the concert. Of course that means that skiing today'll be a bit shorter than you might have liked, but I promise you'll still get a load of exercise. I've got a table booked in a restaurant just across from the palace for a quick dinner afterwards. Sound good?'

Zoë and Juliet nodded enthusiastically.

'I'm beginning to see how your company has grown so fast. You are so organised, Billy.' Juliet's voice was full of admiration.

'Don't you believe it, Jules.'

Zoë could see his eyes smiling, even if the rest of his face was buried beneath layers of insulation. It really was very, very cold. Even with her thickest tights under her thermal trousers, her bottom was frozen, let alone any exposed skin.

'I've just got some very organised people working for me. Besides, when it comes to organisation, the girl beside you has always been the one.' He nudged Daniela and explained, 'Back at number 23, it was always Zoë who used to buy the milk, pay the bills, bully us into coughing up our share. If it hadn't been for her and her constant chivvying, the washing-up would never have got done and we would probably have been suffocated by all the dust. I remember it well.'

'He's right, Zo. Without you, they'd probably have cut our electricity supply off.' Juliet's voice was muffled, but just audible.

'Without that electric fire in the lounge, we'd have died of cold. I can't believe we lived in a house without any heating.' Billy was smiling again. 'Do you remember the ice formations on the inside of the bathroom window?'

'On the *inside*?' Daniela sounded horrified. 'I come from the south of Italy, but even down there we had central heating.' She shuddered. 'I can't believe it. You English are crazy.'

'Not totally crazy. Number 23 was spartan all right, but it did have one big advantage.' Zoë gave her a wink. 'It was cheap, and we were all broke.' She looked across at Billy. 'It must seem so strange to you now.' She had been about to say, 'now that you're so rich', but it felt almost improper, so she cut the sentence short.

'It does, but we all survived. Thinking back on it, it certainly was pretty primitive.'

They reminisced for a while about the mouse holes in the skirting boards, the oven that produced black smoke every time they used it, and their landlord who appeared to spend his entire life stoned out of his head. Yes, Zoë thought to herself, it had been primitive all right.

'Still, we had some good times at number 23, didn't we?' She felt quite nostalgic, frozen bum or no frozen bum. 'Just think, that was ten years ago. So much has happened since then. Billy's become the biggest thing since sliced bread, Jules has been saving people's lives, Mandy's brought life into the world, Imogen's bagged herself a banker and started her own business, and Lorna's on course to reach her century.' She didn't need to specify a hundred of what.

'And you're taking the world of journalism by storm.' Juliet pulled her scarf down a fraction as the chairlift came out of the trees into the early-morning sunlight, and her voice became a bit clearer. 'How is the job? Not getting you down too much?'

'Like I said, it'll do as a stopgap, although I'd be lying if I said I enjoyed rubbing shoulders with some of the people I have to interview.' Thoughts of Ron the photographer came to mind. 'Come to think of it, some of the people I work with are pretty dodgy too. When I get back after Christmas, I'm going to sit down and look for something more appealing.'

This might also be because her failure to file a story about Billy would by then have got her into her editor's bad books, but she didn't mention that. Instead, conscious that nobody had mentioned Grant and determined to show her resolve – whether real or imaginary – she carried on in a normal voice. Or what she hoped sounded like a normal voice.

'And then there's Grant. I've no idea how he's getting on. He looks as if he's okay, but I don't know how things are going for him work wise.'

Grant's jobs had always taken second place to his leisure pursuits and, in consequence, his career had been chequered, to say the least. He had been employed by at least five different firms since university.

'I think things are working out for him at last, Zoë.' Billy's bush telegraph was still working well. 'He told me last night he's finally got himself a job he loves – working for a holiday firm who specialise in water and winter sports. Right up his street.'

'Good for him.'

'He didn't mention his personal life, though. Somehow I didn't get the impression he was seeing anybody at the moment.' Billy sounded a bit hesitant. 'But I didn't like to press him.'

Zoë was surprised. She had been convinced Grant would be shacked up with somebody, even if the original woman had disappeared from the scene. Still, she told herself firmly, his life was of no interest to her any longer, though she realised she really was pleased that things were working out for him on the job front. Maybe if he managed to get his working life sorted out, his personal life would follow. It was about time.

At the top of the chairlift, they skied off together and Billy led them across the hillside, taking a succession of shorter lifts and skiing down a number of the runs they had done yesterday. As Zoë followed him, she was very impressed. She knew she was a pretty good skier herself, but Billy was in a different league altogether. He moved with the sort of natural ease on the skis that you only really develop if you start as a young child. Every turn he made was exquisitely under control – stylish and accomplished. It was hard to believe that this was the same geeky boy who had barely been able to talk to her without blushing all those years ago.

She would never forget one memorable evening back at number 23. She had been coming out of the freezing-cold bathroom wrapped in a big bath towel when in her usual clumsy way she had managed to trap the corner of the towel in the door. As Billy appeared down the stairs, she had started to walk towards him, leaving the towel behind. She had been mortified, blushing to the roots of her hair as she scrabbled for the towel to cover her nakedness. When she finally looked up, however, he was even redder than she was. The embarrassment she had been feeling was clearly as nothing compared to his.

Here, on the slopes, however, he came into his own.

After a while, they reached the bottom of the long lift that climbed all the way up to the rocky summit of the mountain. Zoë and Juliet had debated trying it yesterday, but had decided to wait a day or two. According to their piste map, it looked like the only way back down from there was via a difficult run. Ski runs were colour-coded to show their level of difficulty, from easy green, through blue and red intermediate, to the most difficult – black. The run back down to the hotel was indicated on the piste map as black. Juliet had felt she should get in some more practice on something easier before trying it. But when she mentioned her reservations to Billy, both she and Zoë were surprised to hear his response.

'Don't worry, Jules, we aren't coming back.' He grinned at their expressions. 'I mean, we're not coming back on this side of the mountain. From the top, we can ski over into the next valley on fairly straightforward runs – nothing dangerous, I promise – and then come back by train.'

'By train? What, a special mountain railway?'

He shook his head. 'No, the bog-standard ÖBB – Austrian Railways. There's a tunnel that links the two valleys. Sound like a plan?'

They all agreed and, after a brief wait in a short queue, he led them onto the lift. This was composed of four-seater gondolas – little bubbles enclosed within Perspex windows. In consequence, it was a whole lot warmer than the chairlift, which was just as well, as Billy informed them it climbed to well over two thousand metres. In the relative warmth of the gondola, they were able to strip off their hats and gloves and open their jackets.

As they climbed steadily up the ever-steeper mountainside, now punctuated by jagged outcrops of rock, Zoë could see ski and snowboard tracks snaking down below them. She wondered whether Billy would bring her up here for their off-piste adventure in the following days. It looked exciting and it was certainly steep enough to present a real challenge.

The top station was quite scary – perched on bare rock, with a near vertical drop as the black run set off back down towards Bad Bergstein. Fortunately, as Billy had said, the other side was a good deal less daunting, with much more gentle slopes and a magnificent view across serried ranks of mountains over the border and into Italy. They had a marvellous long run all the way down to the next village. By the time they reached the bottom, Zoë's thighs were burning, but she was as happy as she had been for a long,

long time – and she still hadn't fallen over even once. She carved to a halt alongside Billy and lifted her goggles.

'Billy, that was amazing. Can we do it again, please, please, please?' She adopted Bella's voice and was pleased to see him grin back at her.

'We certainly can. But how about something to drink first?'

Nobody objected to that idea in the slightest, so they unclipped their skis, stacked them along with a load of others in a rack, and headed into a welcoming-looking cafe.

Billy turned towards the others as they walked in.

'You know the best thing about having changed from glasses to contact lenses? I can walk into a place like this from the freezing cold outside and I don't steam up. I remember in the old days, I would go virtually blind until I wiped the condensation off.'

'Mind you, at number 23 sometimes it was as cold indoors as it was outside. There was more risk of your glasses being frozen to your face some nights.' Juliet gave him an approving look. 'But getting contacts was a good move. You look good without the glasses, Billy.'

Zoë smiled to herself as she saw him blush.

She glanced at the clock on the wall and saw that it was half past eleven. Billy also noticed and he suggested getting something to eat with their hot chocolate while they were there. By now, breakfast was a distant memory so, at his suggestion, they ordered another local speciality – *Salzburger Nockerl*. This turned out to be a highly calorific eggy soufflé that appeared on the table looking like a series of pointed mountain peaks. As they ate the wonderful sweet pudding, Billy explained that this place – like Bad Bergstein – wasn't just a winter sports resort.

'This area's great for mountain biking. Once the snow melts, you can go all over the place on old shepherd's tracks and, if you're feeling lazy, you can take your bikes up to the top on the lift and then ride down again. Personally, I think that's cheating, so I try to ride both ways – up and down.'

'Do you like mountain biking, Daniela?' Juliet spooned a mouthful of cream from the pyramid on top of her hot chocolate into her mouth and gave a blissful smile.

'I'm not a very good cyclist, to be honest. Although I'm okay on skis, my balance isn't that great.' She caught Zoë's eye and smiled. 'I believe that's something you and I have got in common, Zoë.'

'Yes, I'm a bit wobbly on a bike as well, but not just on a bike – I seem to have a knack of tripping over my own feet even when I'm on solid ground.'

Billy leant over the table towards Zoë and Juliet.

'Well, if you girls come over to see me in the spring or summer – and I do hope you will – Zoë, you and Daniela can take Arnie for walks, while Juliet and I go cycling. That's your thing, isn't it, Jules? Weren't you saying you'd bought yourself a new bike?'

'Yes, but it's a road bike. I've never tried mountain biking, though it's something I've always fancied. You'd better not ask me twice, or I really will come over again next year.'

'Please come over. There, I've asked twice. You're committed – and the same applies to you, Zoë.' He transferred his attention to Daniela. 'Are you okay, Danni? You've hardly touched your pudding.'

'To be honest, I don't feel too good. In fact, I think I might head back to the hotel and have a lie-down. The station's just down that road there. I can jump on a train and be home in ten minutes.'

'Then I'll come back with you.' He sounded suddenly concerned, and Zoë joined in immediately.

'We'll all come back with you.' She had no intention of leaving a poorly Daniela all alone, even if this would mean missing another long, sweeping run down the mountain.

'I've got a better idea.' Juliet held up a hand to silence Billy before he could interrupt. 'Why don't I go back with Daniela? I'm really feeling my legs today and I want to have a long, hot bath before going to the concert. You two stay and ski some more – besides, without me holding you back, you'll be able to go much faster.'

Billy and Zoë protested, but Juliet was adamant – even invoking the D word.

'I am a doctor, after all.'

There was an ÖBB timetable at the bar, and they saw that there would be a train in less than a quarter of an hour, so the decision was taken. Daniela and Juliet would return to the hotel, leaving Zoë and Billy to ski down from the top once again.

As the two girls went off, Billy and Zoë climbed up to the cable car that connected this little village with the top of the mountain. It was a bit scary, as they were now hanging a long way above the slopes, but it whisked them up to the top a lot quicker than the lifts on the Bad Bergstein side of the mountain. They did the full run twice more and, by the end, Zoë's thighs felt as if they were on fire. Finally, at just after one o'clock, they skied down to the station and bought tickets for the short train ride through the tunnel back to the hotel. There was a train expected in about twenty minutes, so they took seats in the crowded station cafe and ordered coffee and water. As they sipped their drinks, they talked and Zoë learned more about her host.

His main residence nowadays was apparently in the hills above Silicon Valley in California, but he told her he was spending more and more time in Europe. As he talked, Zoë took a closer look at him. Unlike the old days at number 23, he now had colour in his cheeks, and she noticed his eyes for the first time. Back when she had first known him, they had always been hidden behind the heavy glasses – besides, it had been very rare for him to approach any woman close enough for her to discern his eye colour. They were, she now realised, a rich blue – not dissimilar to the colour of the sky outside. Not for the first time since arriving here in Austria, she realised that Billy had morphed into a very good-looking, charismatic man. Presumably Daniela hadn't been the only woman attracted to him. Mind you, she thought once again, the fact that he was also a billionaire certainly didn't detract from his appeal.

The journalist in her realised that she was accumulating some real golden nuggets of information for a revealing article in *HC* magazine – if she chose to write it. But the more she thought about it, the more she knew that she would prefer to lose her job than infringe upon Billy's personal space. And this was not just because he was being so amazingly generous, but because she genuinely found herself liking him more and more.

After a while, the conversation moved to more personal matters and she asked him why it had taken him so long to find the right woman to marry. He shook his head slowly as he answered.

'I don't know. The thing is, it's taken me years to come out of my shell. I told you this is just a veneer, and you have to believe me. I've *had* to become a bit more outgoing, more articulate. As the company grew, I've had no choice, but it's been a real struggle. I suppose it's only now that I've finally found a little bit of self-confidence, but – I'm not joking – it's wafer-thin.'

'You sound fine to me. And I'm delighted you're so happy with Daniela.'

He nodded. 'I know. It's important to find the right person, isn't it? I read an article once saying that everybody's got only one perfect mate out there somewhere. The trick is to find that person.'

'Some trick.'

Her tone must have betrayed her.

'Did you think that was what you'd found with Grant – if you don't mind my asking?'

Zoë nodded cautiously.

'I suppose I did. Of course with everything that's happened in the past year it's all got a bit blurred in my head, but yes, I think I genuinely did believe he was my soulmate – if you'll excuse the cheesy expression.'

He smiled back at her. 'You can say "soulmate" if you like. I'm a man, but I'm a sucker for all that stuff – the pursuit of true love and so on. As for Grant, he seems very attentive, very caring this week. I don't remember him ever being like that when we lived at number 23. My memories are more of him only being interested in rugby and having a good time, rather than being particularly caring towards you. But now he's different. Danni was wondering whether he might be harbouring thoughts of trying to get back together with you. Do you think that's so?'

Zoë took a mouthful of coffee before replying. Billy was right. Grant was a very different – or pretend different – man here in Austria.

'I've been wondering the same myself.'

'And if he is, how are you going to respond?'

She was still trying to formulate a reply when they were interrupted.

'Hi, you two. Are you getting the 13.22 as well?'

It was Fergus. Automatically Zoë's eyes flicked around the room and she soon spotted Grant at the bar. Taking advantage of his temporary absence, she caught Fergus's eye.

'Hi, Fergus. I'm glad I've seen you. I just wanted you to know that my decision to go and sit on the opposite side of the room this morning had nothing to do with you – I was just trying to avoid your breakfast companion. I'm sorry if I appeared rude.'

'Not at all, but thank you. I quite understand the situation. For what it's worth, Grant's done nothing but talk about you since I met him. Even out in the snow you appear to be all he has on his mind. He's a really good boarder, but he's had three spectacular wipeouts today and I'm sure that was just because he wasn't concentrating on where he was going. No prizes for guessing what, or who, he was thinking about.'

'Here, Fergie. Your beer. You won it fair and square.'

Grant materialised alongside their table with two beers. His eyes flicked momentarily across Zoë's face.

'You two already got drinks? Sorry, I didn't see you there when we came in.'

Zoë said nothing, so Billy answered for them.

'We're fine, Grant, thanks.' He swilled the last of his coffee round the cup and then swallowed it. 'Fergus was telling us you've made a few head-first excursions into the snow today.'

'And don't I know it! I've just been shaking whopping great chunks of ice out of my clothes before they start melting.' He glanced sideways at Zoë. 'What about you, Zo? Had a good day?'

'Fine, thanks.' She kept her eyes on her coffee.

Just then, before an awkward silence could develop, the station loudspeakers coughed into life and Billy checked his watch.

'Come on, guys. Train's coming.'

Chapter 9

Seeing as they were going to be in the minibus and then the concert hall, Zoë decided to wear her smart dress again, this time with her good leather knee boots. They had smooth soles and she knew they would be useless on ice, so she made sure she bagged Juliet as soon as she emerged from the lift at five to three.

'Hi, Jules, I'm going to need your arm again, if you don't mind.'

'I don't mind, but I'm not sure how much help I'm going to be.'

Zoë glanced down and saw that Juliet too had opted for a skirt and boots with a bit of a heel.

'Well, if we fall, we fall together.' Zoë grinned. 'Just like last night – apologies once more for that.'

'No problem. I just hope my tights are thick enough and the heating in the minibus works. I didn't bring a long coat – just my skiing jacket.'

'I've got the same problem, but I'm sure we'll be okay. Billy said the restaurant's close to the concert hall and we're being ferried there by minibus. How's Daniela? She got back all right? Any idea how she is now?'

'She'll be fine. She's maybe just a bit tired. This mountain air knocks the stuffing out of you, doesn't it? I stayed with her and chatted for a bit and she was quite cheerful.'

At that moment Daniela herself appeared, accompanied by Billy. Zoë noticed that they were both dressed smartly and gave a silent sigh of relief that her instincts had been right.

'Hi, Daniela, feeling better?'

'Much better, thanks. I just needed a rest. Billy tells me you two had a great time this afternoon.'

'I certainly did.'

As she spoke, Zoë realised that this hadn't just been because of the skiing. Billy really had blossomed into very good company and she had enjoyed spending time with him. She glanced across at Daniela. Yes, apart from being young, tall and beautiful, she was a very lucky girl to have bagged such a lovely man.

The trip down to Salzburg on the meticulously swept roads took just over an hour, and once they got there, as promised, the driver gave them a whistle-stop tour of the city. As Mandy had travelled down earlier in the day with Imogen and Lorna, Zoë sat beside Bella, with her dad on the other side. She found she enjoyed the sensation of being a surrogate mum. She pointed things out to the little girl, listened to her cries of excitement and amazement, and did her best to answer her endless questions about everything from why snow was white to what a Mozart was. As she did so, she surprised herself. For just about the first time in her life, she felt what could only be explained as maternal instincts rising up inside her. She heard Grant's voice from the back row of seats and gave a surreptitious sigh for what might have been.

Salzburg was a delight. The minibus took them past wonderful parks filled with snow-covered trees, many of them festooned with Christmas decorations and lights.

They threaded their way through the narrow streets, also decked with Christmas decorations, past one stunning baroque building after another. And all the time above them was the magnificent fortress perched on a craggy rock, dominating the town. Seen from the banks of the wide river, the rooftops of the town were punctuated by a multitude of church spires, almost all of them in traditional style. This consisted of a square tower surmounted by an onion-shaped cupola and topped with a pointed turret. The result was a skyline that couldn't have been anywhere in the world but Austria. The whole city – and it wasn't big – was crammed with statues, memorials, historic buildings and people. The streets were full of locals as well as tourists, out and about enjoying the Christmassy feel of this cultural hotspot.

One common denominator soon emerged – Mozart. Salzburg was clearly very proud of its most famous son, and everywhere they went, they saw references to him. Zoë lost count of the number of shops, cafes, restaurants and hotels they passed whose names recalled the great composer, and when the minibus dropped them off in the centre of town, the shop windows continued the theme. There were Mozart pencil cases, Mozart T-shirts, even Mozart umbrellas, as well as box after box of confectionery – in particular a chocolate speciality apparently called simply *Mozartkugeln*, Mozart's Balls. Clearly, the good folk of Salzburg were happy to profit from every single part of him.

They rendezvoused with Mandy, Imogen and Lorna in the lobby of the Mirabell Palace, and Zoë felt almost sorry to relinquish Bella's hand to her mother. It had been fun being *in loco parentis* for a little while. However, the sheer magnificence of the palace soon took her mind off her nascent maternal instincts. It was dark by now, but even if it had still been daylight, they wouldn't have seen much of the spectacular ornamental gardens because of the fresh snow. The palace itself was an impressive building, vaguely reminiscent of Buckingham Palace, and here too the Christmas theme was repeated outside and inside with a huge tree, garlands of fir branches and pine cones, and candles. Zoë wondered idly what Health and Safety would make of the potential fire hazard. They found themselves in the midst of a symphony of marble floors and high, often frescoed ceilings with – as Billy had told them – gold leaf glittering everywhere. It was a spectacular piece of architecture, with more than a hint of bling.

To get them in the mood for the concert, they drank fizzy Austrian Sekt at the bar before going into a remarkably cosy concert hall. The cosiness was no doubt partly thanks to a massive majolica stove, almost the height of the room, and partly because the place was packed. It wasn't a big, impersonal auditorium so much as a wide, but not very deep, reception room, with rows of gilded chairs lined up in front of the performers. The seats Billy had booked were right in the middle and were close enough for them to see the sweat on the musicians' brows and the loose hairs hanging off the ends of the bows. It was all very quaint and not in the least stuffy or daunting.

The music was performed by a string quartet, with occasional violin soloists, and the acoustics of the room were excellent. Although Bella drifted off to sleep in her mother's arms after her day on the slopes with her dad, the others all appeared to enjoy it, and Zoë came out at the end feeling quite dreamy. It had been a novel – and unique – experience and she was humming to herself. Lorna, at her elbow, was quick to point out what that signified.

'Am I right in assuming you enjoyed that, Zo? You sound really happy.'

Zoë nodded and found herself smiling. 'It was charming. And yes, you're right. I am feeling happy.' She lowered her voice. 'Apart from the lovely music, I suppose it's the relief of finding that I don't have to put up with Grant's new woman and the fact that it's far easier than I'd thought it would be to get on with him.'

'You look good with a smile on your face. I was worried when I first saw you at Heathrow. You looked terrified.'

'And I *was*.' She grinned. 'I was worried about you too. But I'm delighted to see you looking a lot happier yourself now as well. Maybe it's the mountain air.'

Together they joined Billy and Daniela in the magnificent lobby of the palace. Zoë gave them a big smile.

'Thank you so much. That's a first for me. I've never been to a real live classical music concert before and I loved it. And what a setting!'

'It was stunning. Brilliant.' Lorna joined in and Zoë was really pleased to see her looking so cheery. The others added their thanks and appreciation and Billy looked pleased and maybe a bit relieved.

'I'm so glad you enjoyed the experience. I thought it would make a bit of a change from snow and beer. Right, now hang on and let's see if we can do this without falling over.' He took Daniela's arm in his left and Zoë's in his right and marched them towards the doors. 'The restaurant's only a block away and the city authorities have done a great job of clearing the snow, but hold on tight anyway. Here we go.'

Zoë saw Juliet grab hold of Daniela's other arm for support, and then felt a hand on her free arm. She turned and saw that it was Grant. Before she could object, he gave her a smile.

'With Billy on one side of you and me on the other, you'll be fine. We can't have you falling over on the cobbles.'

'I can manage, Grant.' She thought about pulling out of his grip but decided he was probably right – if she were to fall over, it could spoil the evening for everybody. In the end, she didn't object, but avoided any more eye contact with him.

Assisted by the two men, she managed the short walk without falling, although negotiating the cobbles in her heels did require a bit of care and attention. As promised, the restaurant was barely five minutes away, and as soon as they got there, she withdrew her arm from Grant's grip and murmured a brief 'Thank you.' Deep down, she had to admit that the feel of his hand on her arm hadn't been anything like as unpleasant as she had feared. What this meant was something she wasn't prepared to start considering at this moment. There would be time for that later.

Unusually, the name of the restaurant had nothing to do with Mozart, but it was a fine old *Gasthof* with low beamed ceilings and a series of interconnected rooms. As ever well organised, Billy – or one of his staff – had booked a table in one of the smaller rooms, and they had it to themselves. Here, too, there was a fine ceramic-tiled stove belching out heat, and they stood round drinking excellent local draught beer or sparkling Sekt while the waitress took their orders. On Billy's recommendation, most of them went for goulash accompanied by dumplings. Zoë couldn't help commenting.

'Austrian food isn't exactly low in calories, is it? Hot chocolate comes with a huge pile of cream on top, the choice of cakes is amazing, and the meat dishes are good hefty mountain food. How come the Austrians don't all look like the Michelin man?'

'They don't call them calories for nothing, Zo.' Dr Juliet was the first to respond. 'A calorie is a unit of heat energy. Even if you're just sitting about doing nothing, you need far more calories in a cold climate than a warm one. Throw in the fact that we've been out in the fresh air, taking fairly strenuous exercise all day, and I reckon we can safely eat whatever they serve us and not end up overweight – at least, that's my excuse and I'm sticking to it.'

When they sat down at table, Zoë scrupulously avoided Grant and found herself sandwiched between Mandy and Lorna. She was soon hearing all the details of how they had spent their day. By the sound of it, they had had a really good time, seeing the numerous sights of Salzburg, although Mandy had a strangely distracted air. At the end of the meal, as they were all getting to their feet, she surprised Zoë by gripping her arm and pulling her close enough to whisper in her ear.

'Zo, could you and I talk some time – in private? I always used to turn to you for support and advice back at university, and I need a bit of both now.'

Intrigued, Zoë was quick to agree.

'Any time, Mand. I tell you what, why don't you come to my room when we get back? I'm in 607.'

'Thanks, Zo. I will.'

All the way home in the minibus, Zoë found herself wondering what might be on Mandy's mind, hoping it was nothing serious. It was half past ten by the time they reached the hotel, and Martin volunteered to take Bella off to bed. Mandy came straight to Zoë's room, where she sat down on the sofa against the side wall and took a deep breath before launching into her tale.

'You see, Zo… it's about Martin and me.'

Zoë was genuinely surprised. She had very definitely got the impression that all was going so well for the little family. Mandy and Martin had always seemed to be an ideal couple.

'Is there a problem with him?'

Mandy shook her head. 'No, the problem's with me.' She cleared her throat before continuing. 'You see, Zo, I did a very stupid thing.'

'We all do stupid things from time to time, Mand.'

Mandy nodded absently. 'I know, but I've been *very* stupid.' She took another deep breath. 'Three months ago, back in September, I had an affair.'

Now Zoë was properly surprised.

'An affair?'

'No, not an affair really. It wasn't even a one-night stand. It was an afternoon in bed with another man.' She hesitated. 'An old friend I just happened to bump into. It's not important who it was. We had lunch together and then one thing led to another. I don't know what made me do it, and I didn't even enjoy it that much. But the fact is that I did it, and I've been feeling like a worm ever since.'

'Have you told Martin?'

Mandy shook her head.

'Are you going to tell him?'

'I don't know, Zo. That's why I need your advice. Part of me wants to tell him everything – how stupid I've been, how it meant nothing to me – and beg for his understanding and forgiveness. The other part of me – the cowardly part – thinks I shouldn't say a word.' She looked up from the floor and caught Zoë's eye. 'I love Bella and I love Martin. I don't want to do anything that might hurt them or split us up.'

Zoë leant back against the back of the sofa, turning the revelation over in her head and wondering what to say. Of all her friends, Mandy was just about the last one she might have expected to do anything like this. And now, being asked to give advice put her in an awful position. What if she told Mandy to reveal all, and it resulted in the destruction of their marriage? Alternatively, what if she told her to say nothing, and the shame continued to eat away at Mandy until she had some sort of breakdown? To buy herself a bit of time, she tried a few questions.

'This man, this old friend, do you have feelings for him?'

'No, not at all – and I didn't even then. Like I say, it was a moment of madness. I really don't know what made me do it.'

'Did he know you were married?'

Mandy nodded. 'Oh yes.'

'And it didn't bother him that he was sleeping with somebody else's wife?'

'Not in the slightest.'

'He doesn't come out of it looking too good, does he?'

'I know, but neither do I.'

Zoë could see tears in Mandy's eyes now, so she reached out and stretched an arm around her shoulders.

'Don't cry, Mand. We'll talk this thing through. Tell me something. Do you really, honestly, think Martin's the one for you?'

Mandy nodded her head against Zoë's shoulder.

'No question, Zo. I know I love him. That's the thing. If I didn't, I wouldn't be in such a mess. I love him and I love my daughter – and he loves us. He and Bella have had a wonderful time this week and we've all been so happy together. If I broke up with him, I'd be ruining everything.'

'Sorry to labour the point, but just to be sure – are you saying you want to stay with him?'

'Yes, absolutely.'

Zoë looked around the room, her mind inevitably filled with all the thoughts that had been plaguing her since Grant's departure. Ever present was the nagging doubt that she had somehow been at least partly responsible for Grant's infidelity and his decision to leave. She had been working so hard in the preceding months and as a result had maybe been neglecting him. Had this been the problem with Mandy?

'Mand, you must have thought about this a lot. Tell me, did you come to any conclusion about what made you do it? Are you *sure* you and Martin are made for each other? Or was there something missing in your marriage?'

Now it was her turn to take a deep breath before speaking. 'What about in the bedroom?'

Mandy was sobbing now and Zoë hugged her tightly. It was a while before she was able to reply.

'We still had sex – we still do, sometimes – but to be honest, it was getting purely mechanical and it just wasn't doing it for me.' She wiped her nose with the back of her hand and Zoë passed her a tissue from the box on the bedside table. She looked up at Zoë and blushed. 'If the truth be told, I haven't really enjoyed it for I don't know how long.'

'What about that afternoon in September?'

Mandy shook her head violently. 'Not a thing. I felt nothing but shame and disgust at myself.'

'Well, you can take comfort from that.' Zoë was trying to phrase things very carefully. 'Let's face it, Mand. If you had suddenly felt the earth move that afternoon, you could have pointed the finger at Martin for being unable to make it happen. But you now know that that's not it. As far as sex is concerned, you can get help and advice from therapists or your doctor – or Jules, even. I'm sure she'd be able to help.'

'I was wondering about that myself. You don't think she'd mind?'

'Of course she wouldn't. That's what friends are for. I tell you what, don't let's make any decisions until you've spoken to her. Why don't you try to get her alone tomorrow – maybe while Martin and Bella are skiing – and then you and I can talk again when you feel like it. All right?'

Mandy nodded and gradually regained her composure. Zoë made herbal tea for both of them and they took their time over drinking it. By the time Mandy left, it was close to midnight and, after a long day, Zoë was dying to get some sleep. As soon as she heard the door close, she changed into her pyjamas, slipped into bed, slid down under the duvet and reached out to switch off the light. As she was drifting off to sleep, she found herself wondering if the next knock she would hear would be Grant again. And if it was, how would she react?

Chapter 10

If Grant knocked on her door that night, she heard nothing. In fact, she must have gone out like a light and it was already seven thirty when she opened her eyes and stretched. She kicked back the duvet, got up and went across to the window. This morning there were a lot of grey clouds in the sky and it looked as though the promised snow was on its way. She and Billy had been talking about going off piste today, but she wondered if he might prefer to wait for the fresh powder snow tomorrow. She flexed her legs and was pleased to feel her thigh muscles a lot looser and almost pain-free. She went into the bathroom with a smile on her face.

At the reception desk opposite the lift, Erika had been replaced this morning by one of the male staff members she recognised from downstairs. She gave him a smile and risked a bit of A-level German.

'Good morning. Is this Erika's day off?'

He gave her a smile. 'You speak German? Excellent. Yes, I'm on duty today. Erika will be going snowboarding, I have no doubt. She loves it.' He had a noticeable Austrian accent but Zoë was delighted to be able to understand him pretty well all the same.

She glanced at his name badge. 'And what about you, Marcel? Are you a skier or a boarder?'

He shook his head. 'I'm a skater. Now that the lake has frozen over, it's a fabulous natural ice rink. You should try it. They've got skates down there for hire.'

Now it was Zoë's turn to shake her head. 'Not for me, I'm afraid. My...' She racked her brains for the German word for 'balance'. 'I keep falling over. I'm no good on bikes either.'

'Ah, you have *Gleichgewichtsstörung*. But you can ski, no?'

Zoë felt better about not having been able to come up with the correct term. When it came to long, complicated words, German was quite some language.

'Yes, I can ski surprisingly well. I know it's weird. I've been skiing for two days now and I haven't fallen over yet. But I've almost lost count of the number of times I've fallen over when I'm just out for a walk.'

'Don't speak too soon. Everybody falls over on the slopes sooner or later. But if you're going skiing today, you'd better go out early. The forecast's for heavy snowfall, starting late morning and lasting all afternoon.'

'Thanks for the warning, Marcel. I'll be careful. I don't want to be caught in a white-out.'

This had happened to her a couple of times in her skiing career and she knew only too well the disorientating effect of the horizon disappearing and snow and sky merging into a single entity. People had been known to die in such conditions. However, her German certainly wasn't up to explaining something like 'disorientation' to Marcel, so she gave him a smile and a wave and headed into breakfast.

Juliet was already there, sitting at a table with Fergus. Zoë helped herself to fruit salad and juice, ordered another omelette, and went over to join them. It looked as though Juliet had just arrived and Fergus was just finishing.

'Morning, you two. Did you sleep well?'

'Hi, Zo. Yes, like a log.' Juliet gave her a smile. 'Fergus has just been telling me he dreamt he was playing the violin with Mozart.'

'Playing very badly.' Fergus looked up from his plate and grinned. 'And Mozart was giving me a really hard time – like Imogen does when she's in one of her moods.'

Zoë decided not to pursue that topic. 'Are you coming with us today? I've just been told there's a big dump of snow on its way, so we'll only be out this morning.'

He nodded. 'Yes, I think the plan is to come with you and Billy for an hour or two, and then we're meeting Erika – you know, from the reception desk. Grant's palled up with her. She's a mad keen boarder and she's going to show us a place where there are a bunch of jumps. We'll be all right if we're with her, even if it does start to chuck it down with snow.'

Just for a moment Zoë found herself wondering exactly what kind of pals Grant and Erika were, but she did her best to dismiss the thought. Surely what her ex did was no concern of hers now. Or was it?

She returned to the matter in hand and did her best to sound matter-of-fact.

'That'll be fun, I'm sure, but the word is that the snow's coming late morning, so we'd better watch out. I'm sure Imogen wouldn't want to lose you.'

'You'd hope so, wouldn't you?' There was a funny expression on his face as he wiped his mouth with his napkin and stood up. 'Anyway, I'll see you shortly, girls.'

As he left the room, Zoë and Juliet exchanged looks.

'That was a bit strange.' Juliet sounded puzzled. 'Do you think there's trouble there?'

'Goodness knows. Imogen's a prickly character. No doubt we'll find out more as the week progresses.'

They both fell silent for a few moments, before Zoë changed to a more cheerful subject.

'So what's the plan for today, Jules? You're up for a few hours' skiing before the snowstorm, aren't you?'

Juliet nodded cautiously. 'Yes, but only if we stay on the main runs, and preferably close to the bottom. I don't want to be caught out by the snow high up on the mountainside. What about you? Are you going to be all right skiing with Grant?'

'I'll be fine.' For a moment, the same old doubts about Grant came running through her head. Surely she was just plain crazy to be even thinking about giving him a second chance after everything that had happened. She put on a brave face. 'We'll be a big group this morning and that lessens the chances of me finding myself alone with him.'

Zoë's omelette and cappuccino arrived and she settled down to eat. Juliet, though, was clearly still thinking about Fergus's comment.

'Maybe you should have a word with Imogen, Zo. Check that everything's all right with her and Fergus. You always used to be our agony aunt at uni, didn't you? We all came to you with our problems from time to time.'

Zoë snorted. 'I'm hardly the best person to give advice after the train wreck of my own relationship. I couldn't even spot that my man had got another woman.'

'Not at all. Anyway, you and Grant have both moved on. Spread your wings and fly again.'

'I hope he has. He's being unexpectedly nice.'

Juliet glanced up at her. 'Do you seriously think he's trying to get back together with you?' She sounded sceptical.

'No... Oh, I don't know.'

'But you wouldn't want anything more to do with him, surely?'

'No, of course not.' Zoë crossed her fingers under the table.

'If you want my opinion, he's after anything in a skirt.'

'I'm sure you're right.'

Thought of Erika crossed Zoë's mind once more, but she did her best to shrug it off. As for Imogen and Fergus, in spite of what Juliet had said, she had no intention of getting involved with somebody else's marital problems unless they asked her. She had enough on her plate with her own uncertainties – not to mention Mandy's.

–

Billy and Daniela, along with Fergus, were waiting for them in the lobby when she and Juliet came down at eight thirty, and Grant turned up five minutes late – as usual. Billy confirmed what Zoë had been expecting. They would stay on the pistes and ski until mid morning, at which point Grant and Fergus would go off to meet Erika if the weather conditions allowed, while the rest of them would stop for a coffee in the restaurant at the top of the chairlift. That way, if the snow arrived early, they would be able to take the lift back down to the hotel.

This time, Zoë found herself sitting on the chairlift with Juliet on her right and Grant on her left, Grant pressed hard up against her in the cramped conditions. She did her best to ignore the sensations this produced in her and chatted mostly to Juliet, who must have realised she was finding Grant's proximity challenging and did her best to keep the conversation going. In one of the inevitable lulls, Grant was quick to intervene.

'If we get a load of fresh snow, that should make the conditions tomorrow really awesome.'

Zoë was relieved to take refuge in that British staple of talking about the weather.

'Yes indeed. Hopefully Billy and I will be going off piste tomorrow.'

'Maybe Fergie and I could come with you. You wouldn't mind, would you, Zo?' His tone was hesitant, his expression almost shy. 'I wouldn't want you to feel awkward.'

'Of course not. Mind you, on skis I'd leave you behind anyway.'

'We'll have to see about that. Remember that race we had in Val d'Isère? I beat you hands down.'

For the first time in her presence he sounded animated. She couldn't help replying in kind, and she saw him smile.

'You cheated. We agreed we'd stay on the piste and you took a shortcut.'

'All's fair in love and ski races.' An expression of contrition dawned on his face as he suddenly realised what he had said. 'Sorry, Zo, I didn't mean that about love.'

He turned away and she got the definite feeling his remorse was genuine. Maybe he really was changing.

It was noticeably a little bit warmer today and Zoë was sweating by the time mid morning arrived. There were already snowflakes swirling in the increasingly blustery wind as the two snowboarders disappeared to meet up with Erika. Billy, Daniela, Juliet and Zoë went into the

Zum Wilden Hirsch. The array of tempting dishes on display behind the counter was mouth-watering. Today, however, very few people were out on the terrace braving the snow and, as a consequence, all the tables inside were jam-packed. After a bit of deliberation, they decided to ski down while they still could.

Back at the hotel, they met up in the lounge for coffee and found Imogen, Mandy, Martin and Bella already there. There was no sign of Lorna, nor, of course, of Grant and Fergus. Presumably the two men would be out in the soft stuff with Erika for a while yet. Arnie the Labrador, who had been snoozing in front of the stove, leapt to his feet as he spotted them and came running over to his master and mistress before jumping up to greet Zoë. She felt rather privileged to be selected, particularly as Bella also came running over to grab her by the legs and hang on – almost sending her flying. Luckily Juliet and Daniela were on hand to catch Zoë by the arms and stop her from falling.

Zoë went over to a sofa and sat down, accompanied by the dog and the little girl. Bella immediately climbed up onto her lap and Arnie would have followed suit if his master hadn't yanked him away by his collar.

'Not on the furniture, Arnie. We've been through all this before. Dogs stay on the floor. Got it?'

Reluctantly, the Labrador subsided at Zoë's feet and busied himself with trying to undo her laces. These shoes were fairly ancient, so she let him get on with it while she had a chat to Bella. As before, she enjoyed the little girl's company and that same regret at what might have been came back. It would have been nice to have her own family, but of course that had all been knocked on the head by Grant – unless he really had seen the light and changed his behaviour completely. Nice as he was trying to be, she had her doubts that he was really capable of making such a fundamental transformation. Stifling thoughts of Grant, she remembered last night's conversation with Mandy and murmured a silent prayer that she and Martin would sort themselves out.

'So how come you aren't at ski school, Bella?'

'Reeker says we're going to have a snowstorm, so we all had to come in.'

'*Ulrike* is Bella's ski instructor,' Martin clarified. 'Mine's called Robert and he said the same thing. Apparently there's going to be a blizzard.'

Zoë looked out of the window and saw that it was now snowing a good bit harder, although not yet really blizzard proportions. By British standards, maybe, but not up here in the mountains. The trees along the drive were still visible, although the town itself had already disappeared behind a white curtain.

'So what are you going to do today if it's snowing, Bella?'

'Daddy and I are going swimming, and I think Mummy said she's coming too.'

'Of course, I'd forgotten about the pool.' Zoë looked across at Billy. 'Did I read that it's thermal water?'

He nodded. 'That's right. It emerges from the rock at a constant twenty-six degrees. It's a bit sulphurous, but we've had it tested and it's quite pure – they say you can even drink it if you like. Down in the town there are a couple of places where they offer "cures". As far as I recall, that involves drinking vast quantities of water and spending a lot of time in the toilet as a result. It supposedly cures all known ills – and a few they haven't discovered yet. Anyway, I'd advise you not to drink our pool water, but it is lovely and warm. You should give it a try.'

Zoë glanced across at Juliet. 'Fancy a swim this afternoon, Jules?'

'That's an idea. Somehow I don't think we'll be going out for a while.'

'At some point this week I've got to go into town to buy Christmas presents.' Zoë looked across at the Christmas tree and nudged Bella. 'Do you think Father Christmas will realise that you're here and not at home this Christmas?'

Martin answered for her, winking surreptitiously at Zoë as he did so. 'We've already sent a letter to Father Christmas explaining the situation. He replied, telling us he's on the case.'

As for the shopping, Daniela passed on the news that there would be a Christmas market in the old part of town at the weekend. Zoë and Juliet exchanged glances – that sounded like the perfect place to buy a few presents.

Juliet brought Zoë a hot chocolate, with the obligatory pyramid of cream floating on the top, and they all sat around chatting as the snowstorm outside intensified to very definite blizzard proportions. The wind whipped the snow against the windows and caught in the corners of the frame. Visibility outside was by now almost zero, and Zoë was very thankful they had come in when they had. She spared a thought for any skiers still out in these conditions. It looked really scary. Among them, quite possibly, were Grant and Fergus, and she hoped they would be all right. Surely Erika would have had the good sense to come back before it got really bad.

It was just after midday when the door opened and Erika – still wearing her heavy boots and woolly hat – came rushing into the room. She was alone.

'I'm sorry to disturb you.' She pulled off her hat and twisted it nervously in her hands. She was panting, as if she had been running, and she looked upset. 'We have a problem.'

'What is it, Erika?' Billy took her by the elbow and led her to a seat. 'What's happened?'

'It's Grant and Fergus. I've lost them.'

Zoë saw Imogen sit bolt upright at the sound of her husband's name.

'What do you mean, lost them?'

'We were out in the woods.' She glanced up at Billy. 'Near the *Steinbruch*. We were doing a last run through the trees as the snow really started to come down hard, and I lost contact with them. I was in the lead and when I got to the bottom and turned round, they'd gone.'

'You think they've got lost?'

Erika held up her hands helplessly. 'I don't know. One minute they were there and the next they'd disappeared. I shouted and shouted, but got no reply. The thing is, William, we were quite near the edge of the *Steinbruch*. If they'd headed a bit to the left of the track, they might have gone over the edge.'

'What's the *Steinbruch*?' Imogen's tone was very worried now. She jumped to her feet and came across to stand by Erika.

'It's an old quarry.' Billy looked round the room. 'I'm afraid it's pretty deep.'

As he explained, Zoë found herself feeling as worried as Imogen sounded. So Grant had left her for another woman. So he had hurt her badly. So he was a callous, selfish bastard. The fact was that she had loved him once and now, hearing that he might be in danger – or worse – she felt an unexpected surge of affection for him and fear for his safety. She lifted Bella off her lap and stood up, carefully dislodging the dog from the position he had taken up across her feet as she did so. She went over to Billy, Erika and Imogen.

'Should we inform the authorities – mountain rescue or whatever?'

Erika looked up. 'I've already done that. I told them down at the bottom of the lift and they're sending a snow-mobile out to search for them.'

'Is there anything else we can do?' Imogen was rummaging in her bag. 'Here, I'll try phoning Fergus. Oh God, I hope nothing's happened to him.'

Even amid her own anxiety, Zoë was pleased to hear real affection and concern in Imogen's voice. Maybe she cared for her husband more than she showed.

They all waited as Imogen made the call, but almost immediately she shook her head.

Zoë reached for her own phone and called Grant, for the first time in a year. It rang and rang but nobody answered. For a moment she had an image of him lying broken at the bottom of a cliff, the snow slowly burying him under its weight. As she struggled to stifle the rising feeling of panic that threatened to overpower her, she felt a hand grip her shoulder.

'It'll be all right, Zo.' Juliet's tone was reassuring. 'They're both experienced. I'm sure they'll be okay. All they need to do is keep heading downhill and they'll come to the railway line, if not some houses.'

Zoë nodded gratefully and did her best to sound resolute. 'Thanks, Jules. I'm sure you're right. We just need to be patient.'

As they sat there waiting for news, Zoë found herself feeling unexpectedly anxious. She had come here to Austria unsure whether the sight of Grant would infuriate or depress her, but it had done neither. He had behaved himself impeccably ever since the first moment she had seen him. Even when he had come to her bedroom door and she had sent him packing, he hadn't protested or sulked. He really was giving the impression of being a thirty-three-year-old behaving like a thirty-three-year-old, rather than a thirteen-year-old. He was also looking good, and if she was honest, she would have to admit that she still felt at least a hint of the attraction that had once drawn her to him. What if something had happened to him? How would she feel?

She got up and went over to help herself to a glass of water and she sipped it as she peered out of the window into a featureless white miasma. The conditions were getting worse, and she couldn't subdue a feeling of real concern for Grant's well-being. For Fergus as well, she told herself firmly. Not just Grant. Imogen was standing by the other window, so she went over to her and stretched an arm around her shoulders.

'They're experienced skiers, Imogen. They'll be all right.'

'Oh God, I hope so.' Imogen buried her head against Zoë's chest as she dissolved into tears of apprehension. For a moment, Zoë almost followed suit, but she managed to stem the flow and do her best to think positive thoughts. Of course they would be all right. They had to be.

The waiting felt interminable, and the tension in the room grew by the minute. Imogen gradually recovered her self-control and wiped her eyes, but she didn't desert her position at the window, even though all that was visible was an ever-deepening layer of snow on the window ledge. Beyond that there was just an impenetrable white curtain. After a while, Zoë released her hold on her shoulders and returned to the sofa, where the company of the little girl and the dog was very comforting. She settled down to wait, doing her best to think happy thoughts.

At last, maybe an hour or so later, there was the sound of voices in the corridor and the door opened to reveal Fergus and Grant. Both were still dressed in their outdoor clothes, covered in snow and bathed in sweat.

'Fergus!'

Imogen went rushing across the room to envelop him in her arms. She pressed herself against him and Zoë could see her shoulders shaking as she sobbed into his chest.

Zoë herself felt such an immediate sense of relief that she was already leaping to her feet to go and hug Grant in her turn when she was beaten to it. Before she could make a move, Erika went running over, threw herself into his arms and hugged him with relief – or maybe something more than relief. Zoë turned away and took a couple of deep breaths, then walked over to the window, followed by Juliet.

'You okay, Zo?'

Zoë just nodded, not trusting her voice.

'At least they've both come back safely.'

Zoë nodded again as she heard Billy's voice.

'Erika, why don't you go and tell the mountain rescue people to call off the search?'

Zoë heard running feet then, a few seconds later, she felt a hand on her arm.

'Sorry if I worried you, Zo.' It was Grant.

By this time her heartbeat was starting to return to something approaching normal. She turned to face him. He looked exhausted, his hair plastered against his scalp – presumably either sweat or melted snow. He looked so vulnerable, so different from his usual confident self, that she almost reached out and hugged him, in spite of what she had seen with Erika. But she didn't.

'I'm glad you and Fergus are safe. What happened?'

'I hit a branch and it knocked me flying. As I fell, I took Fergie with me. It was snowing like hell and by the time we'd found my board buried under a deep drift, Erika's tracks were already covered. By then it was an almost complete white-out, so we stuck under the trees, where at least you could see a few metres ahead, and finally made it down to the railway tracks. Then we had to walk.' He hesitated. 'It was nice of you to be concerned for me.'

'I was concerned for both of you. Now, I think I'm going to have a drink.'

She and Juliet went over to the bar and helped them-selves from an open bottle of champagne. Zoë swallowed hers in one go and then spent five minutes hiccuping. By the time the hiccups had calmed down, so had she. By now, Fergus and Imogen had disappeared, as had Grant, and Zoë settled down once more on the sofa, doing her best to quell the tangled emotions in her head.

Zoë looked down. Bella and Arnie were locked in mortal combat on the floor at her feet, so she poked them with her toes, deliberately doing her best to sound cheerful once more.

'Here, no fighting before lunch. You'll spoil your appetite – although seeing as you're a Labrador, I imagine that's impossible for you, Arnie.'

Both faces looked up and Zoë felt that same maternal pang. Yes, it would be nice to have a Bella – and an Arnie.

'Are you coming swimming with us, Zoë?' Bella looked up at her from the floor.

'When are you going?'

Martin answered for his daughter. 'Now. We'll have a late lunch. Otherwise, if we eat first, we'll have to wait for an hour or two before going in the water.'

'You go on. I think I'll go back to my room and change. I might go for a swim later on this afternoon.'

After chatting to Lorna and Juliet for a while, Zoë excused herself and went back to her room to have a bath and wash her hair. As she ran the water, she added a few more notes to the page on her laptop about Billy. It was beginning to develop into quite a list, and she knew she would have to approach him about it before too long. One thing she was fully convinced of now was that she would only send something to Damien if Billy approved it.

That done, she stripped and went through to the bathroom. As she lay in the bath, she did her best to analyse her own emotional dilemma. The inescapable truth was that when she had feared Grant might be in danger, she had been worried, very worried – the sort of worried you only get for somebody you love. Of course she *had* loved him, but did this maybe mean that she still had feelings for him, in spite of her best efforts to stifle them? Almost in the same breath, the image of Erika throwing herself into his arms appeared in Zoë's mind, and she shook her head in annoyance, splashing water onto the pristine bath towel neatly folded beside her. It wouldn't surprise her in the slightest if he and Erika had hooked up. If he could do it with the Claire girl while still living with her, he could definitely do it now that he was a free agent. However, if he really was a free agent, why was he being so affectionate to her, even to the extent of convincing Fergus that he wanted her back? Was that really what was in his head?

More importantly, what was in hers? Could it be – now that he was acting much more grown-up and had apparently found himself his dream job – that he might have changed? Could she really forget the hurt he had caused her and consider trying to make it work again?

Was he worth it?

–

After a lovely buffet lunch in their private dining room, at the end of which Zoë had been unable to resist the temptation to have a large helping of *Salzburger Nockerl* with plum sauce, she retired to the lounge and watched *Casablanca* with Juliet and Lorna. At the end of the movie, wiping the tears from her eyes as Ingrid Bergman flew away from Humphrey Bogart forever, she got up and looked out of the window. It was still snowing heavily and the branches of the trees along the drive were bowed down under the weight. It definitely wasn't the afternoon for doing her Christmas shopping, so she made a quick decision.

'I fancy a swim. Anybody interested?'

The other two shook their heads, pleading laziness, so Zoë went back to her room, collected her costume, pinned her hair up and set off on her own. She took the lift down to the lower ground floor and, as the doors opened, she could immediately smell the thermal spring water. There was just a whiff of sulphur in it – not enough to be repellent, but definitely enough to put her off the idea of drinking it. She found Georg – the staff member who had welcomed them upon their arrival at the hotel – on duty. He gave her a welcoming smile and addressed her in German.

'Good afternoon, Fräulein Lumsley. My colleague Marcel tells me you speak good German.'

Zoë blushed. 'Good afternoon, Georg. Only schoolgirl German, but it's nice to get a bit of practice. So, tell me how this all works.'

He issued her with a big fluffy towel with *Grand Hotel Schlossberg* emblazoned upon it, and showed her the way through to the luxurious changing rooms. She changed into her costume, folded her clothes away into a locker and slipped the key on its rubber bracelet around her wrist. Then she went through into the pool, hoping it wouldn't be too busy. Predictably, as most outdoor activities were off the agenda because of the snow, there were quite a few people – mainly kids – in there, but it was a surprisingly big pool and she found she could swim a good few lengths without too much disturbance, doing her best to keep her hair dry as she did so.

She was on her seventh length when she felt a touch on her bare shoulder. She turned to find Grant bobbing up and down behind her.

'Hello, Grant. Recovered from your ordeal?'

He nodded, obviously glad she was speaking to him.

'It wasn't a big deal, really. I think Erika panicked a bit. We weren't in any serious danger. Listen, is this a good time for us to talk?'

'Treading water in the middle of a sulphurous pool, surrounded by screaming kids? Why, I can't think of anywhere better. Besides, what have we got to talk about? I sent you your half of the deposit on the flat months ago, and you collected all your bits and pieces while I was down at my mum's last winter. What else is there to discuss?'

She let herself drift gently towards the side of the pool and caught hold of the ladder. As she climbed out of the water, she could feel his eyes on her body and once again found herself feeling confused. Whatever her pragmatic self might think, she couldn't ignore the fact that she actually found his gaze nothing like as objectionable as she had imagined.

She was so thrown by this realisation that she evidently wasn't watching her step. Alternatively, it might just have been her usual clumsiness. Whatever it was, as she turned to walk to where she had left her towel, her foot landed on what she later identified as a child's discarded armband, her leg shot sideways, and she was catapulted unceremoniously back into the pool, filling her nose with water and soaking her hair. As she returned to the surface, coughing and spluttering, she felt Grant's hands catch hold of her.

'You okay, Zo?'

She spat out a mouthful of sulphurous water and splashed out of his reach.

'I'm fine. Thank you.'

This time, as she climbed out of the pool, she could not only sense his eyes on her, she could still feel the touch of his hands where he had grabbed her. She carefully avoided the armband and made her way back along to a series of shelves carved out of the bare rock, where she had left her towel. She picked it up and set about drying herself, starting with her hair. A few moments later, she heard his voice and looked out from the folds of the towel.

'How about here? For our talk?'

Seeing him bare-chested, she realised that her hunch that he had been working out was correct. He was definitely in better shape than he had been for a good few years. In fact, he looked really rather good. Burying her face hastily in her towel once more, she replied in a resigned tone, 'If you must, then here's as good a place as any.'

She wrapped the towel primly around herself and sat down on a stone bench, deliberately at the far end of it. She saw an expression of relief on his face, but he respected her wish to keep space between them and took up position at the opposite end of the bench.

'Thanks, Zo.' There was a pause during which he was presumably marshalling his thoughts. 'Look, it's like this. This time last year, I wasn't thinking straight. What I did to you was unforgivable, despicable.' He paused again and looked up, but she wasn't going to make this easy for him.

'You keep on going. I'll stop you if you say anything I disagree with.'

'I think I was going through some sort of mid-life crisis – well, early mid-life. I suppose I thought that by finding myself a younger woman, I'd suddenly, magically, turn the clock back. But it doesn't work like that.'

'No, it doesn't.' Zoë could hear the acid in her own voice, and no doubt so could he.

'Anyway, my relationship with Claire only lasted a couple of months and I've been on my own since then. I didn't want anybody else. I realised – and I feel all the

more certain now – that it's you I want, Zo. Only you…'
His voice tailed off.

'Is that all you wanted to say?'

'Um, yes. So I'm asking if you could find it in your heart to forgive me and take me back.'

She knew there was no way she was going to give him an answer right away, so she shook her head and stood up.

'Right, then, if you've finished what you needed to say, I'm going to have a shower and wash my hair for the second time today.'

'Will you think about what I've said? Please?'

'Of course I'll think about it, Grant. But if you could only begin to imagine what I've been through these past months, you'd know that the chances of me saying yes are very, very slim indeed.'

She pushed her way out through the glass doors and disappeared into the ladies' changing room before he had the chance to say anything else. She didn't stop for a shower, but towelled herself dry, dressed, and went straight up to her room to take another long, hot bath and let her mind roam over everything he had said.

Chapter 11

A couple of unexpected things happened that evening.

First they discovered that the chef had prepared something a little different for them. True to the international nature of the hotel's cuisine, dinner that night was Swiss rather than Austrian. When they all sat down around the big dining table, they found that they were having a fondue evening. Zoë hadn't had fondue for years. She remembered her parents had been given a fondue set years ago before she was born, and they had used it once or twice when she was still a little girl before relegating it to the back of a cupboard in the kitchen, where it presumably still lay to this day. Since then, she had always thought of fondue as the sort of thing Austin Powers might have had on his menu.

However, here in the middle of the mountains, surrounded by deep snow, it suddenly no longer looked like an anachronism. The chef had prepared two types. There was cheese fondue, with cubes of bread that they speared onto long forks and dipped into melted Gruyère and Emmental cheese specially imported from Switzerland. There was also the other type, *fondue bourguignonne*, where they cooked pieces of meat and vegetables in pots of near-boiling oil.

It was towards the end of the meal that the second funny thing happened.

Zoë had been standing up, digging into the melted cheese, trying to rescue a piece of bread that had come unhooked from her fork. After finally locating and removing the offending piece, the regulations the boys had invented for the event obliged her to drink a shot of kirsch as a forfeit. She was by no means the only person to have lost a piece of bread in the course of the meal and, by this time, they were all feeling the effects of a few shots of the powerful cherry liqueur. Imogen had lost no fewer than three pieces and was red in the face and unusually cheerful and relaxed. That in itself was a welcome novelty, but the really odd thing was when Zoë happened to glance down the back of Imogen's designer dress. To her surprise, she spotted a card label still attached to it, peeking out between Imogen's shoulder blades.

She was on the point of drawing Imogen's attention to this when some instinct made her decide against it and she said nothing. Only later, when they were back in the lounge playing Trivial Pursuit, did she mention it quietly to Imogen, so as not to embarrass her in front of the others, and immediately realised that she had been right not to blurt it out to the whole room over the fondue pots. Imogen blushed the colour of a ripe tomato, jumped to her feet and rushed out of the room.

'What's the matter with Imogen?'

Juliet looked up in concern, but Zoë got there first. 'I'll go and see. Maybe the kirsch is having an effect.'

'Don't worry, Zoë. I'll go.' Fergus made to stand up, but Zoë was already on her feet.

'You stay there, Fergus. You're winning. I've got to go to the loo anyway. What's your room number?'

'603. The second on the right.'

Zoë hurried out after Imogen and tapped on the door of Room 603. She had to wait a minute or two before Imogen appeared, now wearing one of the hotel dressing gowns. From the look of her, she had been crying.

'What is it, Imogen? Are you all right?'

She patently wasn't all right, so Zoë pushed past her, walked in and sat down on the sofa.

'Want to talk about it?'

She saw Imogen pause before closing the door and walking reluctantly back to join her on the sofa.

'You've probably already guessed.'

Zoë immediately realised that her hunch had been correct, but she shook her head anyway. It didn't matter – Imogen had drunk enough that evening to be unusually loquacious.

'You saw the label? They've all got them.' Seeing Zoë's expression, she blew her nose, wiped her eyes and elaborated. 'These designer dresses I've been wearing, they're not mine – or rather, in a way they are. You know I told you I've got a boutique in Richmond? Well, these dresses are part of my stock. Have you any idea how much this stuff costs? I haven't got the money to buy this sort of thing for my own personal use, so I borrowed them off the rail, and when I get home, I'll have them dry-cleaned and put them back on display. I thought I'd removed all the labels, but I must have missed one.' She rubbed her hand across her eyes and breathed deeply. 'There... now you know. I'm as poor as a church mouse.'

As she listened to Imogen's confession, Zoë felt terribly sorry for this girl who would always want to be something she wasn't. She reached over and caught hold of her arm.

'Some church mouse! Just think of the value of the stock you must have in that shop. Besides, Fergus is a banker – he's not short of money, surely?'

To her surprise, Imogen shook her head.

'Fergus works for a bank, but he's not one of the fat cats with million-pound bonuses. He's only middle management, not top level.'

Zoë couldn't miss the bitter tone in Imogen's voice and, rightly or wrongly, she decided to pitch in.

'So what? Does that mean you think Fergus isn't good enough for you? You know you love him. Earlier on, when we thought he was lost out in the snow, I saw the worry on your face and the way you hugged him when he came back safe and well. Surely that proves something?'

Imogen sniffed again. 'Of course I love him.' She sounded as if she was trying to convince herself of the truth of her words. 'I'm not saying he isn't good enough for me… It's just that I thought he'd be doing better by now and our standard of living would be higher.'

'Promotion doesn't come overnight, you know.'

'I know. But we've got a big house and a massive mortgage, and all our money disappears into paying that off. My shop's only just breaking even, so we're constantly scraping the bottom of the barrel just to survive.'

'*Survive* in a big house that you *own* in a lovely part of London! Imogen, I'm still living in a rented flat. You're your own boss, and you're married to a good-looking, bright man who's brilliant on a snowboard. I've got nobody. If I were you, I'd sit down and spend a few minutes thinking about just how good your life is.'

Imogen raised her eyes from her fingers, which were playing nervously with the long belt of her dressing gown.

'I know, Zoë, but it's so unfair. Look at Billy. He was the geekiest person I knew at university and yet now he's got all this.'

'And he worked his pants off to get to where he is. Have you ever considered that? I was just remembering how he never went out, never had a girlfriend, and how he was always working. Well, it paid off for him. There's nothing unfair about it.'

Zoë could hear the annoyance in her voice, so she made a conscious effort to be more conciliatory – even if she felt that Imogen was sounding like a spoilt brat.

'You've got a lovely man, an enviable lifestyle – so what if you aren't multimillionaires? If you don't change your attitude, it's going to screw up your life and probably your marriage.'

For the first time, she saw Imogen's expression change from unhappy to worried.

'What do you mean? Has Fergus said something?'

Zoë remembered his comments at breakfast today, but decided not to mention them to Imogen. Instead, she limited herself to some general advice.

'I'm just saying that if you really do love Fergus, it wouldn't hurt to tell him. And to accept him for what he is, not spend your time constantly wishing your life could be better.' She glanced at the alarm clock on the bedside table. It was almost ten o'clock. 'Anyway, come on, wipe your eyes and come back through to the lounge.

Billy said he was going to tell us about the surprise he's got in store for us tomorrow.'

Back in the lounge, the game of Trivial Pursuit was just finishing and Fergus appeared to have won hands down. Bella was snoozing on the floor at her mother's feet, a cushion under her head and one arm stretched across the back of the sleeping dog beside her. As Zoë walked back in, the Labrador opened one eye and it distinctly looked as though he winked at her before giving a hearty sigh, stretching, and resuming his sleep. Martin was sitting next to Mandy, one hand resting on her thigh, and Zoë repeated her silent prayer that Mandy would be able to sort things out.

She went over to the other sofa and sat down beside Billy. He looked up and gave her a smile.

'All well with Imogen?'

Zoë saw Fergus look up as well.

'She's fine. She knows she has to be more careful with her pieces of bread next time she has a fondue. I think the kirsch got to her, but she'll be back in a minute.'

Sure enough, Imogen reappeared a few minutes later, wearing the same dress, but now presumably without the label. Zoë was glad to see her take a seat beside her husband.

Billy tapped his glass to attract everybody's attention.

'Right then, now that everybody's here, I thought I'd tell you what I've got planned for the next few days.' He hesitated self-consciously and Zoë gave him an encouraging smile. 'It's all optional, guys. I don't want anybody to feel they've got to do any of it. If you just want to stay here and chill, please do. Anyway, the weather forecast's good, and with all this fresh snow, the skiing conditions should be amazing.'

A happy murmur ran around the room and Zoë saw Fergus and Grant exchange grins as Billy carried on.

'Tomorrow's Saturday, and there'll probably be quite a lot more people on the pistes, so do be careful. Zoë and I are going powder skiing, I hope.' He shot her an interrogative glance and she nodded vigorously. 'Great. Of course, anybody else who wants to come along is welcome. The next day, Sunday, if you're interested, I thought we might have a go at torchlit sledging in the evening. I hope you'll all come along – and that includes Bella and Arnie.'

At the sound of her name, the little girl opened her eyes, glanced around sleepily and then yawned and stretched. As she did so, the Labrador did exactly the same, and Zoë found herself giggling at the sight of the two of them together.

'How does that sound? Mandy, Lorna, Imogen – they're four-man sledges. No horses this time, just gravity. Are you up for it? We'll come down slowly, I promise.'

Nobody said no, so he carried on.

'Then on Monday, Christmas Eve, we can all do whatever we feel like – maybe try skating on the lake – but remember, in the evening there's going to be the Christmas ball. We've got about a hundred guests staying here and there'll be a few other people coming as well, so there should be no shortage of dancing partners. I hope you've all remembered your ball gowns.'

Zoë exchanged glances with Juliet. She had found what she had been looking for on their shopping spree a few weeks ago, and was now the proud owner of a rather daring long silk dress that had been in the Black Friday sale. It was very sleek, a bit more revealing than her normal choice of clothes, and was a delicate shade of light blue, almost grey. Juliet had pointed out that it would match her eyes. It didn't have a fancy designer label, but it fitted her like a glove and she felt pretty sure she would look okay in it. Juliet had been very complimentary when she saw her in it, so Zoë was quietly confident. Of course, she told herself – not for the first time since buying it – she was only going to be wearing it to look good for her own sake, nobody else's.

She glanced across to Grant. His eyes were trained on her and he hastily looked away as their eyes met. She had spent a lot of time thinking about what he had said in the swimming pool. Did he really believe she would be able to forgive him for all the hurt he had caused her? Was she crazy even to be considering taking him back? Besides, she had made up her mind to avoid men for the foreseeable future and concentrate on her job... hadn't she? Her subconscious refused yet again to give her a definite answer, so she snorted to herself and did her best to change to a simpler train of thought. Christmas was a safe topic, so she turned her attention to Billy's proposals.

'That all sounds fabulous, Billy. What about Christmas itself? Personally I'm not particularly religious, but presumably there'll be a service on Christmas Day.'

'Yes indeed. And there's always a midnight mass the night before, so I expect some people will leave the ball early to go down into the town for that. Christmas Eve is pretty big here in Austria, so some people may go to church in the course of the day too. Personally, I'm not fussed, but if anybody wants to go, it'll be happening.'

Zoë lowered her voice. 'I was wondering about Father Christmas. Will he be visiting Bella's bedroom or coming in here?'

Billy grinned and replied in similar tones. 'I've had a word with Mandy, and the plan is for presents to magically materialise here under the tree once Bella's gone to bed on Monday night.'

'Good old Santa.' She gave his arm a squeeze. 'Of course, you're *our* Santa. I really don't know how to thank you for all this.'

For a moment the old, shy Billy reappeared, before he smiled back at her. 'You're very welcome. It's great to catch up with you all after so long. I'm the one who should be thanking *you* for coming.'

Mandy and Martin were the first to head off to bed, taking a sleepy Bella with them. They were followed almost immediately by Imogen – this time accompanied by her husband. Zoë took that as a positive sign. Pretty soon afterwards, Zoë decided that she too was ready to go back to her room, so she kissed Billy and Daniela and left them to it. Daniela gave her a big smile and Zoë felt really happy for Billy, who had so obviously found himself a lovely wife. She studiously avoided looking across the room at Grant as she left, hoping he would take the hint and not come knocking on her door.

She wasn't very tired – probably because she had only skied for a part of the morning and her trip to the pool hadn't exactly been much of an aerobic workout – so she settled down at her laptop and started to write the article on Billy. She was ever more convinced that the only way she was going to send it to Damien would be if Billy read it first and approved it. With this in mind, she set out to make it as positive and encouraging as possible. Although Billy now displayed an air of confidence, Zoë knew him well enough now to see that it was – as he himself had said – only wafer thin. As she read back through the notes she had jotted down over the past few days, she realised that she had learnt more about him in this past week than in the whole of an academic year living in the same house together. She felt quite ashamed of herself for having taken him for granted back then. Of course, she had been so caught up in the first flush of her new relationship with Grant at the time, she hadn't really been interested in anybody else.

Doing her best to banish thoughts of Grant, she made a start.

For now, she gave the piece the simple title 'The Reclusive Mr Fischer'. Often she only thought up titles for her pieces after they were finished, and sometimes she just passed them up the line and let Damien come up with something suitable. He generally liked far more outrageous and attention-grabbing titles than hers, so she normally just let him get on with it. One time she had written an article about a buxom singer called Betty Bean who had made a mistake at a concert by forgetting the name of the city she was performing in. Zoë's working title for the piece had been, 'Where Am I?'. Damien had renamed it 'Betty's Big Boob'.

The first paragraph was a general introduction, mentioning that she and Billy had shared a rickety old house at university with a group of friends, and describing how hard-working he had been. She debated whether to use the word 'nerd', and then settled on 'geek', which she felt sounded less derogatory. She was far from sure whether she would even go ahead with the article, but if she did, she wanted him to see that it was not intended to be critical – very much the opposite. As she wrote the first few hundred words, however, she rapidly discovered that there was little likelihood of her producing something critical. The fact was that she liked Billy a lot. She always had liked him, but it was only now she was getting to know him properly. And what she was learning about him only served to endear him to her all the more.

By the time she had finished for the night, she had produced the first couple of paragraphs and a rough outline of how she intended to proceed, and so far she hadn't found anything negative to say about him. As she closed the laptop and headed for the bathroom, she felt sure she would be able to produce an article that would be informative for the reader, but also reassuring and supportive to her friend. But she continued to repeat her internal mantra – she wasn't going to do anything with it until Billy had had the chance to read and approve what she had written.

Chapter 12

The snow carried on relentlessly and must have finally stopped some time during the night. When Zoë surfaced in the morning and looked out of the window, she was almost blinded by the sun, still very low on the horizon, as it reflected across the virtually unbroken swathe of white covering the scene outside. She was feeling really excited at the prospect of a day in the powder snow.

The previous night, although she had spent a while turning over in her head everything that Grant had said to her, she had soon drifted off into untroubled sleep. This morning, she was no closer to reaching a decision about his plea to her at the pool, but she didn't care. There was no need for her to make any hasty decisions, and if he didn't like it, he could lump it.

Before going through for breakfast, she checked her emails and found no fewer than three from Damien, prodding her less and less tactfully to get her finger out and send him the article about Billy. She came very close to telling him to stay out of her private life and leave her alone, but discretion won the day and she sent him a reply telling him she was making progress with the article and would try to approach Billy without delay.

She and Billy travelled up on the chairlift together with Daniela and Juliet, and they split up at the top, arranging to meet up again at lunchtime in a small restaurant near one of the other lifts. Billy told them that the place was run by one of his friends, who had promised to reserve them a table outside on the terrace. There wasn't a cloud in the sky and the views from up there promised to be spectacular. As Juliet and Daniela skied off, Billy turned to Zoë with a smile.

'Right, are you ready?' She nodded. 'Then let's go. I'll take it fairly slow at first, but if you want to go slower or faster, just shout. Okay?'

He pulled on his goggles, checked his bindings and then – seeing that she was ready to go – set off directly down the untouched slope beneath the chairlift. The snow was still a bit icy, but it was immensely deep and Zoë found herself having to work really hard, particularly in the turns. Ahead of her, Billy was making it look easy as he snaked down the slope. She followed him, doing her best to mimic his movements. Then, when he reached the first pylon, he suddenly shot off to the left and disappeared into the pine trees.

Zoë took a deep breath and followed him, zigzag-ging through the forest, following his shape as it danced through the virgin snow. From time to time he brushed against snow-laden branches, and she soon learned that it was best to stay back a bit, otherwise she was almost blinded by the clouds of powder snow he released as he passed. After a few exciting and exhausting minutes, they emerged from the trees onto an open area, presumably a bit of high pasture in the summer months. Below them she could just see the roof of a shepherd's hut sticking up from a drift, and she closed up on Billy as he swooped down towards it in a series of wide, elegant curves. At the last minute, to her surprise, instead of going round the hut, he deliberately headed straight towards it, skiing up the slope of the roof, and flying off it into the air. As he became airborne, he threw his arms out to the sides and kicked his legs apart. Even through her woolly hat she distinctly heard him give a hoot of exhilaration.

She hesitated and then made a split-second decision, determined to follow him. She shot up the roof of the hut and found herself flying through the air, her heart in her mouth. To her considerable relief – and pride – she landed perfectly and carved round into a spectacular stop in front of Billy, who was standing waiting for her, a smile on his face. As she stopped, her skis showered him with snow and she felt great satisfaction at seeing him wipe handfuls of the stuff off his face before he could speak to her. She pushed her goggles up onto the top of her head and gave him a broad grin.

'That's for not warning me you were taking me over a jump. That, Herr Fischer, was amazing. I'm pretty sure my whole life flashed before my eyes for a moment back there. You realise you're completely crazy?'

'Rubbish. That's one of the easy ones. Make sure you don't annoy me, or I might take you over the one we call the *Hubschrauber* – the Helicopter. You can probably imagine how it got its name. If you hit it right, you fly for about ten metres.'

'And if you don't hit it right?'

'You still fly ten metres, but the landing's a lot less enjoyable. One guy I was with ended up stuck halfway up a fir tree – and not a small one. It took him ten minutes to climb down.'

'I like fir trees, but I have no desire to end up stuck in one. Sitting around the Christmas tree back at the hotel will do me fine. I'll make very sure I don't annoy you, Billy Fischer, and I'll leave the *Hubschrauber* to experts – or lunatics – like you.'

He smiled back. 'I'm sorry. Taking you over the jump was a bit mean, I admit, but it was fun, wasn't it? You ski really well, you know.'

'It's probably just as well I do, otherwise you might have ended up carrying me home.'

'You wouldn't have hurt yourself. Look – see how deep it is here?'

To demonstrate, he leant on one of his poles and it disappeared all the way down into the soft snow until his glove was touching the ground.

'It always piles up here after a dump like we had last night. I knew you'd be all right.' He tugged the pole back out again. 'So what next? What would you like to do? More jumps? Cross-country? Faster? Slower?'

'I thought that was just perfect, to be honest, Billy. More of the same, please.'

'Excellent. Okay, follow me.'

And off they went again.

She felt very much at ease with him, and was delighted for him that he had finally emerged from his geeky former self – at least on the surface. Now, he was really good company – and a spectacular skier. She very nearly took the opportunity to speak to him about the article when they were on one of the lifts, but at the last moment decided against it. Maybe, she told herself, she wouldn't even speak to him at all, and would just tell Damien he had said no. Billy trusted her and she knew she couldn't let him down.

She found it quite straightforward to follow him down the slopes, and as she did so, she let her mind roam, inevitably returning to the subject of Grant once more. She had told him she would think about what he had said, and she had done a lot of thinking, but now she knew it was time to make up her mind – for his sake, but above all for her own.

As she skied along, it all gradually fell into place. She knew that if Billy chose to lead her over another jump, she would follow him blindly, because she trusted him. She trusted him and he trusted her – she had no doubt about it. But the fact was, she didn't trust Grant. Grant was looking good, he was sounding contrite, but deep down she knew she would never be able to trust him properly again. It was really very simple. Without trust, there could be no relationship, and that was that.

Suddenly all her doubts were extinguished – she knew what she had to do and she resolved to tell him to his face the next time they were alone. As the decision took root in her mind, she felt a great sense of relief and closure. She was smiling as they broke through the edge of the trees and she followed Billy's dancing hips down to the next chairlift. Surprisingly, there was no queue, and they climbed straight on. As they sat down together and drew breath, he must have sensed her mood.

'You're looking happy, Zoë.'

'I *am* happy, Billy. I'm really happy. And it's not just because I'm out here with you on such a perfect day. It's taken me a year, but I think I've finally managed to get over Grant.' She turned towards him. 'You can't imagine how good that makes me feel. And you can't imagine how grateful I am to you for inviting me here to this gorgeous place. It's so clean, so fresh, so unspoilt, and all I have to worry about is not falling off my skis. I've been able to do a lot of serious thinking and I've finally cleared my head as far as Grant's concerned.'

Billy removed his goggles and pulled off his hat, stuffing it down the front of his jacket. The sun was full on them now and it was really quite hot. Zoë could see steam rising into the frosty air from both of them.

'Have you told him?'

Zoë shook her head. 'I'll do that later on today.' A thought struck her. 'If I were the vindictive kind, I'd wait till the day after tomorrow – the anniversary of his bombshell to me.'

'You haven't got a vindictive bone in your body, Zoë – or at least, if you have, I've never noticed it. I'm glad you're feeling good. I've been concerned for you.' He stretched and reached into his jacket for his phone. 'Would you mind if I take a photo of you with that lovely smile on your face?'

'Okay, and then I'll take one of you.'

After the photos, he asked her the same question that had been going round inside her own head.

'So now that Grant is history, what happens next? Jules said you were very busy at work and concentrating on finding something new. Does that mean you're dropping out of the game as far as men are concerned?'

'Some game!' She heard the bitterness in her voice and struggled to change her tone. 'What was it you were saying about everybody having one perfect mate out there somewhere? Maybe mine's still waiting for me, but I'm not holding my breath. I'm not about to embark on another search – at least not for now. For the moment, I'm concentrating on getting things sorted out as far as my career's concerned.' She summoned a grin. 'Of course, I suppose there's always the chance I'll find Prince Charming at the Christmas ball, but I'm not going looking. We'll see what happens.'

At that very moment, something did happen. The lift had been running smoothly along, about ten metres above the ground when it suddenly stopped, so abruptly that the chairs started swinging wildly.

'Don't worry.' Billy was quick to reassure her. 'It's probably just somebody at the top or the bottom of the lift who's got caught up in something. It'll start up again in a few moments.'

In fact, it was a full ten minutes, and by that time Zoë had well and truly cooled down and was definitely relieved to get moving again. When they reached the top, Billy asked the lift man what the delay had been. The answer was delivered with a thick local accent that defeated Zoë, and she had to ask Billy for a translation.

'There's been an accident down near the bottom, apparently. The helicopter's on its way. Listen, that's it now. That was quick – must be serious.'

Sure enough, she heard the unmistakable sound of a helicopter approaching. It flew low over them, following the line of the lift, before disappearing from sight beyond the trees. The engine noise rose as it landed and then silence – or nearly silence – returned.

'Let's hope they're okay. Right, I suggest we get moving. I'm freezing.'

Zoë agreed wholeheartedly, and they set off down through the trees once more. They had a fabulous morning's skiing and reached the little restaurant at the top of the furthest lift bang on half past twelve as arranged. However, just as they were sitting down with Juliet and Daniela on the sunny terrace overlooking the valley, everything changed.

It started with a phone call to Billy.

He pulled his mobile out of the inside pocket of his jacket and answered it, and it immediately became apparent that all was far from well. Zoë and the others waited anxiously for him to reveal what had happened. He gave a series of orders in German to the person at the other end before finally ringing off. Still holding the phone, he explained what he had been told.

'That helicopter we saw – it was for Martin.'

'Martin? What on earth? Surely he was at ski school, wasn't he?'

'Yes, but apparently he lost control as they were skiing down to catch the same lift we took. Before the instructor could get to him, he slid right in front of an empty chair just as it was leaving the bottom station. It gave him a hell of a whack on the head, then lifted him bodily into the air and carried him for ten or twenty metres before the attendant could switch it off. Then it dropped him.'

They were all appalled. Daniela spoke first.

'Is he badly hurt?'

'We don't know. He was knocked unconscious and they say it looks as though his arm is broken. They've flown him down to hospital in Salzburg.'

'How awful!' Daniela sounded horrified. 'Does Mandy know?'

'Yes. That was Georg from the hotel on the phone. He's driving her down to the hospital in the minibus as we speak.' He turned towards Zoë. 'Bella's still at her ski class. Mandy asked if you could go and collect her and look after her until we know what's going on.'

Zoë jumped to her feet and the others followed suit. 'Of course. Can somebody show me the quickest way back?'

Together they skied back to the baby lift by the hotel, where Zoë found a very cheerful Bella, blissfully unaware of the drama. On the way there, Zoë had been rehearsing in her head the best thing to say to a five-year-old. In the end, she decided that there was no point in worrying her until they knew more. As she and Bella walked back to the hotel, she explained the situation in terms that wouldn't frighten the little girl too much.

'Your mummy and daddy have gone to Salzburg – you remember, the place where we went to the concert in that lovely old palace.' Bella nodded. 'Your daddy fell over when he was skiing and he's probably hurt his arm, but we'll know more when Mummy phones to let us know.'

'Will he be all right, Zoë?'

'I'm sure he will.'

Bella looked reassured and didn't notice that Zoë's fingers behind her back were firmly crossed.

Back at the hotel, Zoë dumped her skiing jacket and heavy boots and asked Erika to give her a spare key to Mandy's room. As much to fill a bit of time as anything else, she ran a bath for Bella and saw that the little girl was scrubbed and changed into clean dry clothes. She then took her back with her to her own room, stuck her in front of some cartoons on the television and went into the bathroom for a quick shower. It was past two by the time she was ready and they walked hand in hand down the corridor to the dining room, where they helped themselves to food from the buffet and sat down to eat.

Billy and Daniela arrived as they were finishing their lunch, accompanied by the Labrador, and Bella wasted no time in disappearing under the table to play with him. Billy gave Zoë an update.

'It's pretty good news. Georg just phoned. Martin's conscious and lucid, although they're keeping him in overnight in case of concussion. He's fractured two bones in his arm and he's pretty badly bruised, but he'll be fine.'

'Thank God for that. What about Mandy? Does she want us to bring Bella to see her dad?'

'I asked Georg to ask her. I can easily drive down if necessary.'

They went through to the lounge and found everybody there, apart from Fergus and Grant, who were still out on the slopes. Thought of Grant reminded Zoë of the decision she had taken and the conversation she was going to have with him. She wasn't looking forward to it, but she knew she wouldn't have complete closure until she had spelt it out to him.

There was a second call from Georg at the hospital in which he informed Billy that Mandy would be coming back to the hotel with him in a couple of hours – once Martin's arm had been set and the doctors were satisfied that there were no complications. Zoë relayed the message to Bella.

'Bella, that was the hospital. Your daddy's going to be fine. Your mummy's coming back a little bit later on.

She wants Arnie and me to look after you until then. All right?'

Bella nodded from the floor, where she and the Labrador were playing fetch with an old tennis ball. Zoë was glad to see her looking calm and happy. As she gazed down at the little girl, her heart went out to her and she hoped everything would work out with her parents – not just in terms of the skiing accident. She also reflected how nice it had been to look after this little mite, and as she watched her playing with the dog, she sensed those long-neglected maternal instincts welling up once more. Now that things were irrevocably over between her and Grant, maybe she really should consider getting back into the dating game in the hope of finding her perfect partner, with whom to set about creating a Bella of her own. Once again, though, her subconscious trotted out the usual mantra – concentrate on work and forget dating. There were times when her subconscious could be very stubborn.

Chapter 13

That afternoon, Zoë and Juliet went for a walk with Bella and the dog. Somebody with a tractor had cleared a path that wound its way through the grounds and right round to the back of the hotel. Arnie and Bella ran on ahead, having a fine time chasing the tennis ball from one bank of snow to another. Zoë kept a weather eye on both of them, feeling very grown up. This didn't go unnoticed by Juliet.

'You and Bella seem to be hitting it off, Zo.'

'She's a sweetie.' Zoë turned towards her and smiled. 'I was just thinking how nice it would be to have one of my own – and a Labrador would be rather good, too.'

'Well, getting a dog's easy enough, but for the child, I'm afraid you're going to need help.' Juliet was smiling back at her. 'Not that you need to be a doctor to know that. Of course, you could go for the less messy option – IVF. That way, you wouldn't need one of those big smelly men. Or are you telling me you're beginning to think it might be time to start looking round again for a big smelly man?'

'I don't know. At least I've definitely come to a conclusion as far as one man's concerned.' She saw comprehension on her friend's face. 'That's right. I'm finally over Grant and I'm going to break the news to him tonight, just as soon as I see him. So I suppose that now I've got him out of my system, I might even start thinking about a replacement.'

'Good for you, Zo. You need to move on with your life. How do you intend to go about finding your new special someone?'

'Well, I was telling Billy there's always the Christmas ball the day after tomorrow. Who knows what might happen there?'

Juliet grinned. 'And you could consider sending a letter to Santa. You never know what he might bring.'

'And what about you, Jules? You really quite happy on your own? Aren't you interested in settling down? Surely there must be loads of hunky doctors in that hospital of yours. You are very pretty after all.'

Juliet blushed. 'I'm quite happy on my own for now, and as for hitching up with another medic, I really don't think so. It's a tough life being a doctor these days – for all sorts of reasons. If I were to end up with another medic, I'm sure we'd spend all our time moaning about the NHS. Besides, there really isn't anybody who appeals back there.' She caught Zoë's eye and for a moment her expression became more serious. 'Strictly between you and me, there is somebody I rather like here, but it would be too complicated.'

'Somebody here?' Zoë's eyes opened wide and her mind rapidly flicked through the men in their group. Billy, Martin, Fergus and, of course, Grant. Surely not…?

'Forget it, Zo. It isn't going to happen.' Zoë could hear from her voice that Juliet was already regretting her moment of frankness.

'You can tell me…'

'I could, but then I'd have to kill you. One of these days I promise I'll sit down with you and we can have a long talk.' Juliet was smiling again. 'But for now, like I say, forget I spoke. Nothing's going to happen. As for being alone, it does have some advantages.'

'Such as?'

'Nobody to steal the bedclothes, nobody to nag you for drinking too much coffee or for opening a bottle of Prosecco on a Sunday afternoon. And above all, the freedom to make all your own decisions. No, Zo, I wish you well if you are going to start dating again, but I'm just fine as I am.'

At that moment, a bit further along the path, the boisterous dog knocked Bella into a pile of snow and she emerged in tears. Zoë hurried across to comfort her, and by the time peace had been restored, the moment had passed. She returned to Juliet's side, still turning over in her head just who might be attracting her. Surely not a married man? Of course, Grant wasn't married, but that couldn't be... Could it?

By now the light was beginning to fade and suddenly the fairy lights in the trees all switched on, turning the snow-covered branches into sparkling jewels. Zoë smiled as she saw Bella and Arnie stop as one and stare up in wonder. The lights made an enchanting display and she was reminded that Christmas was just three days away and she still had some shopping to do.

'Jules, what about presents? I'm going to get something for Bella and I really want to get something for Billy as a thank-you. What do you reckon?'

'I was thinking about trying to get a little something for everybody – you know, just a token, nothing major.

I thought we could put the presents under the tree on Christmas Eve, and then on Christmas Day – maybe after lunch – we could open them together.'

'That's a good idea. Didn't somebody say something about a Christmas market?'

Juliet nodded. 'Yes, Danni said there's going to be a Christmas Fair down in the old town tomorrow. I thought I'd go and see what I can find.'

'Excellent. I'll definitely come with you.'

–

Back at the hotel, Zoë removed Bella's coat – or more precisely, she rescued Bella's coat from the middle of the corridor where she unceremoniously dumped it. She then replaced the little girl's boots with slippers and made sure that she washed her hands before taking her through to the lounge for tea. Juliet was already there, and Lorna and Imogen were sitting reading. Zoë went across to sit down near them and Bella immediately climbed onto her lap. The ever-hungry dog sat attentively at their feet, his eyes glued on the cake on the little girl's plate. He had already worked out that crumbs – or even bigger pieces – often fell from her hands.

'You're looking broody.' Lorna set down the copy of yesterday's *Guardian*. In true Austrian tradition, there was a fine selection of newspapers here in the lounge, all attached to wooden handles with hooks on the end and hanging on a special rack for the use of the guests. Unsurprisingly, in a luxury hotel like this, they included a choice of papers in both German and English. There were even copies of *Le Monde* and *Corriere della Sera*. 'So what are you going to do about it, Zo? Thinking of getting back together with Grant?'

Zoë shook her head. 'Nope. That's all over. In fact, as soon as I see him, I'm going to make sure he knows that – although after the way he treated me, he can't really be under any illusions, surely?'

Lorna looked impressed. 'Don't you believe it – I'm sure he came here determined to try to get you back. But good for you. I'm sure you're doing the right thing. So if it isn't to be Grant, does this mean you're ready to get back out there?'

Zoë smiled. Why was everybody so keen to see her hitched up with a man again?

'I'm not sure, Lorn. We'll see. For the moment I'll just concentrate on getting Grant out of my hair and finding a job I like. Anyway, how're you and Imogen doing this week? Not getting bored all on your own while we're out skiing?'

They shook their heads in tandem and Imogen answered. 'I'm having a lovely time. This is the fourth book I've read since I got here, and it's just wonderful to be able to relax and know that there's no need to worry about work, or cooking or cleaning or whatever.'

Lorna nodded in agreement. 'Same for me. I've been able to catch up on a lot of reading and I've been to the pool every morning for a good long swim. I feel a lot better for it.'

Zoë was mildly surprised. There had only been one kind of exercise that had interested Lorna when they had lived at number 23. She took a closer look at her and got the distinct impression that the dark rings beneath her eyes had reduced. She also had some badly needed colour in her cheeks. So this holiday was doing them all good – apart from poor Martin.

A few minutes later, the door opened and Fergus and Grant arrived – still in their outdoor clothes – and made straight for the fridge containing the beer. Grant pulled out two bottles of Stiegl and opened them before passing one across to his snowboarding buddy. He clinked his bottle against Fergus's and took a big mouthful of Salzburg's famous beer.

'What a day! Brilliant, eh, Fergie?'

'Absolutely brilliant.' Fergus emptied half of his bottle down his throat and looked round with a grin. 'So, what's been happening here?'

'You haven't heard about Martin?'

Both men shook their heads, their expressions changing to shock as Juliet explained what had happened. Zoë was pleased to see Grant looking genuinely concerned. This was a good sign of personal development – in the past he had only really been interested in himself. Although this in no way shook Zoë's conviction that she was still going to tell him that things were irrevocably over between the two of them, it boded well for his future – without her.

Just as Juliet was coming to the end of her explanation, Billy and Daniela appeared with the news that Georg had phoned and Mandy was on her way home. Zoë glanced down to check that Bella had heard the news and saw to her surprise that the little girl was fast asleep in her arms. At her feet, the dog was also sleeping, a satisfied canine grin on his face. Bella's plate was still in her hands and it was now completely empty – suspiciously empty. Zoë gently removed it and, on impulse, gave the little girl a gentle kiss on the top of her head.

'So, how was the powder skiing this morning?' Fergus looked interested. 'We saw the two of you at one point and followed your tracks. It looked as if you did a bit of flying.'

'And from what we could see, neither of you fell over. We tried to do the same and one of us didn't quite nail the landing. Kudos, Zo.' There was real admiration in Grant's voice, but she didn't let it break her resolve.

'No, neither of us fell at all today.' She glanced at Fergus. 'So were you the one to end up in a snowdrift this time?'

'And how! A lump of ice even found its way right down into my underpants. Still, we had a lot of fun and we went back up and did it again – this time without incident.'

'I'll show you guys where there are a few more jumps if you like.' Billy led them over to the detailed map on the wall and pointed them out. He then turned back towards Zoë and the others. 'Anybody else for a beer? I could certainly do with one. It's been quite a day.'

–

It was about seven when Mandy arrived back. She was looking weary, but her expression was bright. Bella woke up at the sound of her mother's voice and scrambled down from Zoë's lap to run across to greet her, accompanied by the dog. As Mandy swung her into her arms, she took out her phone.

'Your father made a little video for you, sweetheart. Here, come and take a look, everybody.'

As they all crowded round, Zoë peeked at the screen to see Martin lying in a hospital bed with his left arm in a plaster cast. He was looking remarkably cheerful.

'Hi, Bella. Look what Daddy's done. I told you I was a terrible skier, didn't I? Anyway, I'm fine now and I'll be home tomorrow. Look after Mummy for me. I love you both.'

Zoë caught Mandy's eye. 'He sounds fine. No ill effects?'

'None at all, hopefully – and it's even his left arm he managed to break, so he can still pay the bills with his right hand.' She was sounding upbeat, but Zoë could see the strain around her eyes. As Billy had said, it had been quite a day.

And it wasn't over yet.

Dinner was another international event. This time, the chef had prepared an Italian feast with tasty antipasti, followed by pizza made in the hotel's own wood-burning pizza oven. For dessert, there was a choice of panna cotta or tiramisu. There was ice-cold Prosecco and rich, tawny Barolo to drink with the meal, and Zoë managed to eat a whole pizza by herself. She justified it to her conscience by reminding herself that she had only had a bowl of soup for lunch. She didn't remind her conscience about the portion of wonderful sweet *Kaiserschmarrn* that had followed the soup, but it had been quite a day after all.

Her chance to talk to Grant finally came at the end of the meal. Whether by accident or design, the others all got up and left the dining room, leaving Grant and Zoë all alone at opposite ends of the long table. Summoning her courage, Zoë told him what she had decided.

'You asked me to think about what you said in the pool, Grant. Well, I have done and the answer's no.' Seeing him about to remonstrate with her, she hurried on. 'I've thought long and hard about it, and the bottom line is that I'll never be able to trust you fully again. You may have some idea of just how brutally you treated me – I certainly hope so. If you have, then maybe you'll never treat another girl the same way. But it's not even that. Yes, you hurt me terribly, but it's the lack of trust that's the game-changer. It's definitely all over between us, and please don't waste your time or mine by trying to persuade me otherwise. We're done. All right?'

Of course it wasn't all right and he tried hard to plead his case that he was a changed man. By the end, she almost felt sorry for him, but her resolve held. Finally she stood up and walked over to where he was still sitting.

'You're a good-looking guy, Grant. You're bright – when you want to be. I'm sure you'll find somebody else, and when you do, I hope for her sake you treat her better than you treated me. I wish you well for the future, but it'll be a future without me. Now, I'm not going to let this spoil my holiday. I've been dreaming of Christmas, and I aim to make it a new beginning for me. Who knows, maybe it will be for you too.'

With that, she walked out of the room and back down the corridor to the lounge. Mandy and Bella had already disappeared. Zoë could well imagine that Mandy must be exhausted after the trauma of the day. Imogen and Fergus were sitting together on a sofa and Zoë was delighted to see her hanging onto his arm with both hands, a happy expression on her face. Hopefully this might mean that she was trying to follow Zoë's advice and appreciate her husband for the good guy he was – even if he wasn't a billionaire.

After the stress of her talk with Grant, Zoë didn't need much persuading to accept a glass of thirty-year-old cognac. She cradled the balloon glass in her hands and went over to sit down alongside Lorna and Juliet. As she did so, she exchanged looks with both of them, but nothing was said. Both of them had already understood that the deed had been done. She was pleased to see Grant return to the lounge a little later on and strike up a conversation with Billy as if he didn't have a care in the world. He didn't look across in her direction even once. At least he hadn't taken it too badly so hopefully the atmosphere in the group wouldn't be soured.

They sat and chatted, the Labrador snoring at Zoë's feet, until she felt her phone vibrate with the arrival of a text message from Mandy.

> *Bella's asleep and I will be soon. I'd like to talk to you first, if you can spare a few minutes. Feel like coming round? X*

Zoë replied simply,

> *Of course. Five minutes. X*

Five minutes later, she got to her feet, stroked the dog's head, and said goodnight to the others. When she reached Mandy's door, she realised she still had the spare key that Erika had given her, but she didn't need it. Mandy had wedged a shoe in the door to stop it locking. Zoë picked up the shoe, let herself in and closed the door quietly behind her. She found Bella fast asleep in her bed and

Mandy already in her pyjamas, sitting on the edge of the big bed.

'Hi, Zo, thanks for coming.' Mandy kept her voice low, although Bella looked as if it would take an explosion to wake her.

Zoë sat down and set the shoe on the floor and the spare key on the bedside table before reaching over to catch hold of Mandy's hand.

'How're you doing, Mand?'

'I'm doing fine.' She raised her head and caught Zoë's eye. 'Really well.' There was a pause before she continued. 'I told him, Zo, I told Martin.'

'What – about what happened in September?'

Mandy nodded. 'It was just the two of us in his room after they'd set his arm and he'd regained consciousness. He was sounding very lucid and I could see he was going to be all right. I was holding his hand and I suddenly started crying – probably delayed shock or just pure relief. One thing led to another and I ended up blurting out the whole sad, sordid story.'

'And how did he take it?' Zoë gave Mandy's hand a squeeze.

'Far, far better than I could have hoped. In fact, it was almost as if he was already expecting it. He told me he knew things between us had been getting stale, and that he'd noticed how depressed I'd been. He asked me if this meant I wanted a divorce and I told him no, very much the opposite. Doing something so stupid had made me realise how much I love him. I asked him to forgive me, to try to understand that it was just a moment of madness, that it would never, ever happen again, and how it had actually strengthened my feelings for him.'

'And his reaction?'

'He caught hold of me and hugged me so tightly, he accidentally pressed the alarm button and the nurse came running. Once we'd explained to her that it was a false alarm and she'd left, he told me he loved me dearly and asked me to forgive him for maybe not being as caring and considerate as he could have been. Although things are better now, he said he's had a lot on his plate at work and he knows he should've made more effort at home.'

'So it's all good now?'

'It's all fine. Thank God.'

'Did you tell him who the other man was? Does he know him?'

'He didn't ask and I didn't tell him.' Mandy took a deep breath. 'And what about you, Zo? Are you and Grant getting back together?'

Zoë shook her head. 'No, I told him tonight. It's definitely over and that's that. It's a question of trust.'

To her surprise, she saw a look of relief flood across Mandy's face. Now it was her turn to grip Zoë's hand and squeeze it.

'Thank God for that. I'm so, so glad.' Zoë was still trying to digest this reaction when Mandy looked up from their entwined fingers and straight into her eyes. 'You see, Zo, it was him. My moment of madness last September was with Grant. Now do you see just how screwed up I've been?'

'With Grant?' Zoë felt the air whistle out of her lungs. 'You and Grant?'

There were tears in Mandy's eyes now. 'Ever since we got here, I've been dreading you announcing that the two of you were going to get back together again. I knew I had to tell you, but I've been so scared.'

Zoë was in turmoil. She couldn't work out if she was angry with Mandy or simply shocked. As for Grant, it just made her decision to sever relations with him all the more justified. Her eyes dropped towards her hand, still being held by Mandy, and she shook her head in disbelief. She gave Mandy's fingers a little squeeze, then released them and stood up.

'Thanks for telling me, Mand. You didn't need to. I'd never have found out. Besides, what Grant does is no business of mine.'

'I'm so sorry, Zoë, honestly. I know you and he had broken up, but still, I shouldn't have done it. I've been so, so stupid. Please forgive me.'

'There's nothing to forgive. Really, it's all right. Now I think I'm going to go to bed. I hope you get a good night's sleep.'

'Goodnight, Zoë, and thank you.'

'Goodnight, Mandy. Sleep well.'

Chapter 14

When Zoë woke next morning, she was in no hurry to get up. The previous night, she had been so tired she had fallen asleep almost immediately, but now, in the light of day, snuggled underneath her wonderful cosy duvet, she had time to think back on the events of the last few days – up to and including Mandy's bombshell about the identity of her mysterious lover. The one thing that emerged clearly from the revelation was the confirmation that the decision to tell Grant they were finished once and for all had been the right one. The fact that he hadn't batted an eyelid at the idea of going to bed with one of their good friends, and in so doing potentially ruining her marriage, was sickening. The fact that he had then come along on bended knee, telling Zoë she was the only woman for him and he wanted to get back together with her, was equally unpalatable. She lay under the quilt and snorted to herself.

She didn't have much time for snorting as she heard a gentle noise from the direction of the door. Looking up, she saw a piece of paper emerge under it and she threw back the covers to go and take a look. It was a note from Billy.

Hi, Zoë. Hope you slept well. I'm just going out for a quick walk with Arnie. I'm going to be tied

*up this afternoon, but I wondered if you felt like
skiing to the castle this morning. It could be a bit
of fun. See you at breakfast. Billy.*

Zoë glanced at the time and saw that it was almost half
past seven. The sun was already up and it promised to
be another sparkling, cloudless day. She hurried into the
bathroom.

Before going out, she checked her emails again and
wasn't surprised to see another one from Damien, sent
at half past midnight. There were rumours he slept in
the office, and she could well believe it. This email, like
the three others he had already sent her, was asking how
she was getting on and making a thinly veiled threat of
reprisals if she didn't get the story. She shot off a quick
reply, telling him the article was progressing and she might
speak to Billy about it after the gala ball on Monday
night. As she pressed *Send*, she knew that was a cowardly
response and sooner or later she would have to break the
news to Damien that she wasn't going to go along with
his plan. Although she was still adding to the article, she
was more and more convinced that she wasn't going to say
anything to Billy at all and she would just forget the whole
thing. The more she saw of him, the more she liked him
and the less she felt like invading his privacy.

When she walked into the dining room, she saw Billy
and Daniela sitting with Juliet at a table by one of the
windows. She helped herself to a bowl of fruit salad and
went across to join them. As she did so, a black shape
emerged from under the table and a happy Labrador
jumped up to greet her.

'Morning, Arnie. Morning, you three. Sleep well?'

'Yes thanks.' Juliet caught her eye. 'What about you, Zo? How did it go with Grant?'

Billy looked up from his muesli. 'Grant? Does that mean you two are back together?'

Zoë shook her head decisively. 'Very much the opposite. No, after dinner last night I told him it was all over between us. Period.'

'And how did he take it?'

'Not brilliantly, but he definitely got the message. That's it. It's finished.'

'So now you can begin a new chapter in your life.' Daniela smiled across at her. 'That's exciting, isn't it?'

'Where to from here, Zo?' Juliet also gave her an encouraging smile.

'I'm taking it one day at a time. As far as today's concerned, I'm planning on taking Billy up on his offer to visit the castle.'

'The castle? I didn't even know there was a castle.' Juliet looked to Billy for help.

'Oh yes. Take this hotel, for instance – the clue's in the name.'

Zoë understood immediately. 'Of course – *Schloss* means castle and *Berg* means mountain. But where *is* the castle?'

Billy pointed out of the side window. 'Behind the hotel the ground rises steeply for a long way until it reaches a sort of outcrop with a flattish plateau. Above that, the mountain proper starts. The castle's on that outcrop. At least it was. There was a medieval castle there until it was knocked down by some warlord or other in the seventeenth century. All we'll be able to see are the remains of a tower and a big archway. At this time of year everything else will be hidden by snow, but the view from up there, down over the hotel, the town and the valley, is superb. And getting up there and back down again will be a lot of fun.'

Zoë looked at him suspiciously. 'Fun as in your *Hubschrauber* jump? Or worse?'

'Nothing so dramatic, although the first few hundred metres are a bit steep. Remember when we took the gondola lift up to the very top and then skied over to the other side? Well, this time we ski back on this side. Jules, you're very welcome to join us if you like.'

Juliet shook her head decisively.

'I can still remember how scary it looked. No thanks, Billy. Danni and I are planning something much more sedate this morning, and then Zoë and I – assuming she survives – are going shopping at the Christmas market.'

–

Zoë and Juliet travelled up on the chairlift with Billy and Daniela and then skied with them for half an hour or so as they worked their way across to the bottom of the gondola lift. As Daniela and Juliet skied on, Zoë and Billy took the lift up to the mountaintop. As they climbed ever higher, Zoë began to feel more and more apprehensive – especially as they drew closer to the near-vertical slope immediately below the top, across which they would have to traverse. Billy must have noticed her concern.

'Seriously, Zoë, it'll be fine. It's just that the slope's a bit bare and steep for the first hundred metres or so. After that, it levels out slightly and there are trees.' He reached across and tapped her gloved hand with his. 'Trust me, I wouldn't have suggested it if I didn't think you were up to it.'

Zoë nodded. She did trust him – in fact, she trusted him implicitly. She summoned a nervous smile.

'Thanks, Billy. I'll be fine if you say so.'

'I do say so. I wouldn't ever let anything happen to you.'

It was such a sweet thing to say, she almost leant over and gave him a kiss, but she resisted the temptation, feeling sure it would only make him embarrassed.

When they were standing at the top, looking down, she very nearly turned tail and climbed back on the lift. Below them was a very, very steep slope. It wasn't completely vertical, so it wasn't a cliff as such. It was covered in snow, rather than bare rock, but she had little doubt that if she lost her footing as they traversed across it, she wouldn't stop sliding until she hit the trees a long way below. She felt her throat dry and her heart pound, but Billy didn't give her time to have serious second thoughts.

'Ready? Just follow me and it'll be fine.'

He gave her a wink and then slipped smoothly sideways onto the slope, carving across it on just the inside edges of his skis, his shoulders turned out towards the valley. Zoë took a couple of deep breaths and followed him.

It probably only took a minute or two to get across the slope to the trees on the far side, but she couldn't remember breathing at any point in the process. As she finally skied to a halt alongside Billy, she exhaled and then gasped for air. Glancing back over her shoulder, it looked even steeper. She sucked in a few more breaths as she felt her heartbeat begin to return to normal.

'Brilliant, Zoë. That was perfect. Well done. From now on, it's plain sailing.'

'I haven't been so terrified for ages.'

'Don't be silly. You're too good to fall on a simple slope like that.'

'Simple slope…?'

They set off again and Zoë followed him through the snow-covered trees, gradually curling around the hillside. As predicted, the ground levelled out after a while and she spotted the ruins of the castle poking up through the snow. Billy led her into the middle of the ruins as far as the remains of a massive Gothic arch, half submerged beneath metres of snow. To one side there was an opening in the rocky hillside and he skied right up to it and stopped.

'Coffee break?'

Zoë followed his example, releasing her bindings and stepping off her skis, standing her poles up alongside them. Then she turned and inspected what was evidently a cave in the rock – whether natural or man-made was hard to establish with so much snow covering and softening the edges. A few paces inside the cave it was clear of snow and somebody had had the good sense to install a solid-looking bench. At Billy's invitation, Zoë sat down on it. She had to agree with him – the view really was spectacular. Framed by the rocky entrance to the cave, the whole valley opened up before them and she could see right out over range after range of mountains. Directly below them was the hotel and the town, with tiny ant-sized figures moving about.

'Here, I wasn't joking about the coffee.'

From his backpack he removed a Thermos flask and two cups, along with a plastic box containing two slices of sumptuous chocolatey *Sachertorte*. Zoë felt her smile broaden.

'Wow, that's amazing. Were you in the Boy Scouts, Billy? Be prepared and all that?'

'No. When I was that age, I was building my first computer.' He smiled back at her. 'Apart from my trips over here to see my relatives, I didn't get out into the great outdoors very much. That's why I've got a lot of catching up to do now.'

'I envy you that. I played a lot of sport as a girl, but never really got out into the country either.'

'Well, remember, I wasn't joking when I said you were very welcome to come back in the summer – with or without Juliet. If you like, we could go camping in the mountains. It's amazing the wildlife you see. A few years back they found a brown bear that had wandered over from Italy only a few kilometres from here, but I don't think there are any more of them left.'

'A bear?' Zoë shook her head. 'I'm all for a bit of wildlife, but I draw the line at bears.' She took a sip of hot coffee and eyed her piece of chocolate cake hungrily. 'Still, that's a very kind invitation, and like Jules, I know I'm going to take you and Daniela up on it.'

'If you want to bring your next boyfriend, please do.'

'Somehow I don't think there's going to be one of them for a good long while, Billy. I want to get the whole Grant thing out of my system first.'

'Is that really all over? He looks and sounds very keen still.'

'Not after last night he doesn't – or at least I hope he doesn't. I told him straight to his face that we're history now. And that's absolutely final.' She looked across at Billy, remembering what Mandy had told her. 'For all sorts of reasons.'

'Wow! I was chatting to him after you went off to bed last night and he appeared absolutely normal – not a care in the world.'

'He's a very good actor. To him, lying is an art form.' She reached for the *Sachertorte*. 'It's the lack of trust that's the killer. That sort of thing leaves a nasty taste in the mouth.' She took a big bite of the soft, rich cake, feeling the apricot inside mix wonderfully with the dark chocolate. 'Mmm, talking of tastes in the mouth, this is gorgeous.'

'Glad you like it. Well, I'm happy for you if that's what you want. Besides, I'm sure you'll find yourself somebody else. I've seen the way you look when you're around Bella. You were so good with her while her dad and mum were at the hospital. Perhaps you'll be starting your own family before long.'

'One step at a time, Billy.'

She took another bite of cake and washed it down with a mouthful of coffee. It was a delightful way to spend a morning and she really enjoyed Billy's company, feeling very relaxed with him. After a while, she turned the question round on him.

'So what about you and Daniela? Are you thinking about kids?'

'I'd love kids. I was an only child and I wish I'd had a brother or sister. Yes, I'd definitely like to start a family.'

She noticed that he used the pronoun *I*, rather than *we*. Whether this indicated that Daniela didn't share his opinion wasn't clear, but she decided it wasn't her place to enquire.

'I'm sure they'll be the luckiest of children.' She caught his eye. 'And not just because you've done so well for yourself financially. Somehow I just know you'll make a great dad – although if you take your kids across that cliff we skied over earlier this morning, Daniela will probably – and quite rightly – divorce you on the spot.'

They sat and chatted as they ate their cake and drank their coffee. She told him about her life in London and he told her about life in California. By the time the cake box was empty, they both knew a good deal more about each other. She knew full well that she now had more than enough to finish the piece for *HC* magazine about him, but she also knew she wasn't going to do that. She would be scared stiff of ruining what was turning into a very special kind of friendship, so she decided not to mention it to him. She would just tell Damien that Billy had said no. And if Damien didn't like it, that was his hard luck.

She was just finishing her coffee when she heard Billy whisper, 'Don't move a muscle, Zoë. Look!'

She could barely hear him, but her eyes followed the direction of his pointing finger. At the entrance to the cave there was a sudden movement, and a sinuous shape detached itself from the rock and emerged into the sunlight. It was a gorgeous little furry animal with a dark head, a cream-coloured body and a very white bib under its chin. It was the length of a cat, but much, much lower to the ground, and its tail was bushier even than a squirrel's. She had a vague idea that it was some sort of weasel or stoat, but she had never seen one of either before. It stopped for a moment, stared directly at them and then, with a graceful movement, disappeared behind a snowdrift.

'How beautiful. What was it, Billy? A weasel?'

'Close, but no cigar. That little fellow was a pine marten. We get a lot of them in the forests around here, but we're really lucky to see one so close.'

'Well, better a pine marten than a bear, I suppose.'

'Quite.'

As they stood up again and she watched him bundle the Thermos and the plastic box back into his pack, she knew that her decision not to write the article was the right one. This morning had been so great, it would be a crime to risk spoiling it. Decision taken, she gave him a broad smile.

'Thank you so much for this morning, Billy, terrifying cliff face and all. It's been just perfect.'

He looked back at her with an answering smile. 'And it gets even better. We've now got a vertical kilometre run through some of the finest ski territory anywhere in the world.'

He hadn't oversold the run back to the hotel. There was something very exciting about being the only people skiing through such a large area. They didn't encounter a single sign of any other humans, although there were numerous animal tracks. As the sun hit the trees, an intoxicating aroma of resin was released, and Zoë breathed deeply, relishing the experience. It was stimulating, it was exhilarating and it was very good exercise. By the time they got back to the hotel, her thigh muscles were screaming at her once more, but she didn't care. It had without doubt been the most fun she had ever had on skis.

As they came to a halt by the front door of the hotel, she beamed across at Billy.

'That was absolutely super. Thank you so much.'

'So you've forgiven me for frightening you at the start?'

'Of course I've forgiven you. Now, I'll let you get on. I know you said you're busy this afternoon and it's gone twelve already. Is that a business thing?'

He shook his head. 'No, I'm having tea with my great-aunt. She's in her nineties now and she's in a home in Salzburg. She's a grand old lady, and if it wasn't for her and her husband, I'm sure I wouldn't have been able to ski as well as I do. The least I can do is to pay her a visit around Christmas.'

When Zoë got back to her room, she decided to put her decision into action. Although she had planned to stick with the job at *HC* until she found something else, her loyalty to Billy – especially after all he had done for her this week – was too strong. She sat down and composed a very polite and diplomatic message to Damien explaining how she couldn't go through with the article. She realised that he wouldn't be happy about it, but she couldn't betray her friend's trust. As she pressed *Send*, she felt a combination of fear and satisfaction. It felt good to have had the courage of her convictions, but the prospect of unemployment was scary.

–

The Christmas market was fascinating.

Juliet and Zoë had decided not to have lunch in the hotel, and when they got to the market, they were glad they hadn't eaten. As they made their way down the long line of stalls in the main street of the town, they were assailed by tempting aromas from all sides. Christmas was very definitely in the air and they spotted no fewer than four Father Christmases walking by – one of them kissing a pretty girl in reindeer costume alongside him. Zoë reflected that it was just as well Bella wasn't with them or she would have been very confused. Everywhere they looked, there were streamers, banners, garlands and fairy lights. Somewhere ahead of them a choir was singing carols, and she recognised 'Silent Night' sung in the original German.

They were barely a quarter of the way along the street before their resolve failed and they stopped for a bratwurst. The man at the counter tried to get them to have some Christmas punch, but from the fumes coming off it, it was probably lethal, so they stuck to the local beer. The bratwurst was served up on a cardboard plate, accompanied by a slice of chunky local bread and a big splodge of mustard. They found a place to sit down on a low wall – the snow already cleared by previous diners – and took their time over the succulent sausages, dipping them in the mustard and washing them down with cold, frothy beer.

As they ate, they chatted. Juliet told Zoë about her morning on the pistes with Daniela and how well the two of them were getting on. Zoë nodded in agreement.

'Like Billy and me. He's great company – especially when you think of how quiet he used to be at number 23. And Daniela's a sweetie. They must be so happy together. He was repeating his invitation to come over again when the snow's gone. I'd be up for it. How about you?'

Juliet nodded enthusiastically. 'Just try and stop me. This is a gorgeous place. But if we do come back in the summer, I say we pay our own way. Of course he's absolutely loaded now, but I wouldn't want him to think we were trying to take advantage of his generosity.'

Zoë nodded. 'I agree – assuming I've still got a job by then.'

'Why, Zo? Thinking of chucking this one in already?'

Zoë shrugged her shoulders. She didn't really feel like telling Juliet about the article right now. Instead, she took refuge in obfuscation.

'It's all a bit complicated, but I get the impression my editor's not too happy with me.'

'Why on earth? You're a great journalist.'

'The fact is, Jules, he isn't happy with me because I'm not happy with him. I'll tell you all about it some time. But going back to Billy, it must be really difficult to be so amazingly rich. Not for the day-to-day stuff, of course, but you'd never really know if people were being friendly just for your money. If I was in Billy's shoes, I'd find it hard. I mean, take Daniela, for example. She's young, she's gorgeous, she's bright. She could have pretty much any man she wanted and yet she chose Billy. If I were him, I'd always be worried that somehow she'd married him for his money.'

Juliet nodded. 'I suppose it's something they've discussed, but I know what you mean. I've been spending quite a bit of time with her and there are moments when I find myself wondering the same thing. She obviously likes him a lot and she's very affectionate to him in public, but she doesn't seem in the least bit miffed that you and he have been skiing together. In her shoes, seeing him with an old friend – and a very beautiful one – I'd be a bit wary.'

'She doesn't have anything to worry about with me. I'm not in the market for another man at the moment and I certainly wouldn't dream of targeting somebody else's husband.' As Zoë spoke, she was reminded yet again of

Grant and his casual affair with Mandy. 'But I do think Billy's a lovely man. Do you know, he's off to see his great-aunt this afternoon? That's rather nice.'

'He's a sweetie all right.' Juliet swallowed the last of her beer. 'So, Christmas shopping? Are we ready?'

They set off down the street, stopping regularly to gaze at the host of colourful items on display. There were stalls selling only Christmas tree baubles – some gilded, some hand-painted. There were stalls displaying gingerbread hearts, wood carvings, candles and candle holders. Every other stall appeared to be offering food or drink, from cheeses to honey, and Glühwein to punch. All in all, they spent well over an hour there and finally emerged laden down with Bad Bergstein mugs, cuddly toys, snow globes, mittens and scarves. Back home in England, Zoë had prepared for Billy a blow-up of the only photo of the whole group of them she could find, and she splashed out on a silver frame from an antique stall to hold it. She felt that this was the very least he deserved after his amazing generosity.

At the last minute, they remembered wrapping paper and tape, and had to hunt around until they found some-where that sold it. As they came away with their purchases, they passed a stall selling hand-made jewellery, and one of the smaller items caught Zoë's eye. It was a little silver animal attached to a thin silver chain. Upon closer inspec-tion, she saw that the animal was none other than a tiny pine marten, just like she and Billy had seen that morning. It wasn't too expensive, so she bought it as a present for herself, knowing it would provide her with a memory of that amazing morning on the slopes above Bad Bergstein.

By the time they got back to the hotel, they were both feeling quite dozy and Zoë retired to her room for a snooze. That evening they were supposed to be going sledging by torchlight, and she thought a rest in advance of that might be a good idea. First of all, however, she checked her emails. There was no reply from Damien, and she wondered if this indicated that a storm was brewing back in London. She had already worked out – as had everybody at *HC* magazine – that silence from Damien normally presaged a volcanic eruption of ire. She gave a little sigh and closed the laptop, convinced that her decision not to go ahead with the article was the right one, but still apprehensive.

She had only been lying on her bed for a few minutes when there was a light tap on the door. She immediately thought of Grant and her hackles began to rise. Surely he must have got the message that she was no longer interested. With a sense of dread, she went over and opened it. But this time, it wasn't her ex.

'Hi, Lorn, how're you doing? Everything all right?'

'Sorry to disturb you, Zo. Listen, could I talk to you? I need a friendly ear and probably a shoulder to cry on, and you've always been the one for that.'

From the pained expression on her face, Lorna looked as if she was about to burst into tears at any moment, so Zoë stepped to one side and waved her in, closing the door behind her.

'I was just having a lie-down, so if you don't mind, I'll hop back under the covers and you can come and sit beside me.'

As she snuggled back underneath the cosy duvet, she saw Lorna kick off her shoes and climb onto the other half of the bed. Zoë propped herself up on one of the pillows and looked across at her. Although there was definitely more colour in Lorna's face, she looked worried. Zoë gave her an encouraging smile.

'So, tell Auntie Zo all about it.'

Lorna met her gaze, but didn't manage an answering smile.

'I'm getting old, Zo, and I don't like it.'

Zoë kept the smile on her face.

'We're all getting old, Lorn. That's what happens to us humans, and remember, it's always better than the alternative.' She was deliberately trying to keep her tone light.

'I know, Zo, but I still don't like it. Before too long I'm going to be middle-aged, and then I'm going to be old, and the way things are going for me, I'm going to be old alone.'

'Of course you're not. Besides, we're the same age, give or take a few months, and I'm on my own too. I have been for a year now and I'm not letting it get me down.' As she spoke, she wondered just how honest she was being. Lorna wasn't the only one to worry about being alone.

'I bet you won't be single for long, Zo.'

'I'm in no hurry, but let's talk about you. You're a bright girl, with a great job.' Zoë knew by now that Lorna's career in insurance was on the up. She had just moved to a senior position in a big online company and the prospects sounded great. 'You're very attractive, you've got a lot of experience, and you'd be a real catch for any man.'

Lorna nodded her head remorsefully. 'It's the experience thing that's been weighing heavy on me. There comes a time in life when you realise you're too old to keep on waking up next to random men – and sometimes you can't even remember what their names are. It's true – that's happened more than once. Anyway, about a year ago, I took a good hard look at myself in the mirror and decided enough was enough.' She caught Zoë's eye. 'Yes, I know I still brag about my conquests, but that's just bluster. The truth of the matter is that I wouldn't mind betting you've had sex more recently than I have.'

'I broke up with Grant a year ago. Are you telling me you haven't…?'

Lorna nodded. 'That's right.'

Zoë found herself beaming. 'Well that's great, Lorn. Really. You've decided to make a fresh start with a clean sheet and that's terrific. And now you've got a new job with a new set of people, so you can create your new reputation from scratch. What's so depressing? You should be laughing.'

'There's a problem, though, Zo. There's a man from my wild past who's just sent me an email.' She paused, fiddling with her hair nervously. 'I've known him for years and we used to meet up every now and then for a swingers' party or a dirty weekend somewhere exotic. To be totally honest, we got up to some pretty disgusting things, things I'm not proud of and that I have no desire ever to repeat. I haven't seen him for over a year now and I thought that had all died a death. Until today. The thing is, somehow he's got wind of the fact that I'm here in Bad Bergstein and he says he wants to come over.' Her expression soured. 'To use his expression, he thought he could make sure the festivities go with a bang.'

'So what's the problem? Tell him to take a hike.'

'Is that what I should do?'

'From what you've just been telling me, of course it is. Or are you hankering for another bout of wild sex?'

Lorna shook her head decisively. 'No, not at all. It's just… at least that way I wouldn't be alone.'

'Well I'm going to be all alone at the ball. So what?'

'So you think I should say no?'

'You're the one who's got to decide, Lorn, but from what you've been telling me, it shouldn't be too difficult a decision. If it's a fresh start you're looking for, you need to ditch all the memories of your past. Like I'm trying to do with Grant.' She repeated what she had said to Billy. 'You never know. We may both meet Prince Charming at the ball.'

Lorna managed a grin. 'We can always hope. Thanks, Zo, I'll go now and leave you to your snooze.'

'I'm knackered after this morning's skiing, Lorn. What was that you were saying about none of us getting any younger? Why don't you think about what I've said and we can talk again whenever you like.'

Lorna slid off the bed and slipped her shoes back on. 'I'm sure you're right. I think I'll see what Juliet says as well.' She leant back across the bed and kissed Zoë on the cheek, then headed for the door. 'Thanks again, Zo, I knew I could count on you.'

Zoë lay back and closed her eyes, reflecting on what Lorna had told her. She was delighted that her friend was trying to make such a drastic change in her life and she felt sure it could only do her good. She hoped Lorna would have the courage to tell her erstwhile lover to find himself another sexual partner, and that the gala ball might be able to provide her with a handsome prince – and maybe even one for herself.

Chapter 15

When Zoë arrived in the lounge at five o'clock, Juliet and Lorna were the only ones there, and it was immediately clear what they had been discussing.

'I've been thinking about what you said, Zo, and I'm going to do it.' Lorna glanced across at Juliet. 'Jules agrees. I'll text him, tell him I've changed, and put him off.'

'Good for you, Lorn. I know that's the right thing to do.' Juliet caught Zoë's eye and smiled. 'I see you're living up to your agony-aunt billing, Zo. You see – we still come to you, even now.'

Zoë had been thinking along the same lines, but she hadn't mentioned Imogen's problems or Mandy and her dilemma to anybody. If these two only knew…

'I'm glad I can help. Anyway, it's a two-way street. I know I can always come to either of you if I get myself in a fix. Jules, you were a tower of strength last year when Grant walked out on me. Here's hoping I never need to call on you again for something like that.' She looked round the room. 'So have either of you seen Martin? Wasn't he supposed to be back here this afternoon? Has he been discharged from hospital?'

Juliet nodded. 'Erika told me that Georg brought him back an hour ago. I think he and Mandy are in their room doing a bit of family bonding.'

That sounded very good to Zoë. 'I doubt if he'll be coming sledging, but I hope Bella and Mand can come. Sledging in the dark promises to be a lot of fun.' She checked out the clothes Lorna was wearing and nodded approvingly. 'I see you've got your cold-weather gear on. What time are we going out?'

'Billy's due back from Salzburg any minute now. I imagine he'll tell us. I think the idea was to go fairly early before it gets too terribly cold and then come back here for dinner afterwards.'

Billy and Daniela arrived just after half past five with Arnie the Lab, followed by Imogen and Fergus. Zoë was impressed to see Imogen dressed for the cold.

'Hi, Imogen, so are you coming sledging?'

Imogen looked a bit uncertain. 'Yes, Fergus talked me into it. I told him I'd only come if he came on the sledge with me.' That also sounded pretty good to Zoë. Maybe her agony-aunt talents weren't so shoddy after all. She glanced across at Billy.

'So what's the plan, Captain?'

'As soon as we're all here, we take the lift up to the first station. I've had a word with the guys and they'll keep it running for us. The sledges are up there, along with the torches. Should be a laugh.'

Just then, Mandy, Martin and Bella appeared, with Grant behind them. He gave everybody a smile and a wave as he came in, although his eyes just skated over Zoë, and that was just fine with her. After Mandy's revelation, she had absolutely no desire to talk to him. Ignoring him, she joined the others as they clustered around Martin and checked to see that he really was all right. Apart from a

Technicolor black eye, a surgical dressing on his forehead and his arm in a sling, he looked fine – if a little sheepish.

'Sorry for worrying you guys. It was a stupid place to put a ski lift. Surely they must have known that a moron like me would come along and head-butt it.'

Zoë checked out the plaster cast covering his left forearm. It already boasted a colourful drawing of a stick figure bumping into a large object. In case anybody might be in any doubt as to the identity of the artist, alongside it was written: *I love my daddy*.

'Right, guys, if everybody's ready, shall we head off to the sledges?' Billy glanced sideways at Martin and wagged his finger at him. 'Georg told me the doctors said you're not allowed near a ski lift for at least a couple of months. Are you going to be all right here on your own?'

'He's not going to be on his own.' Mandy touched Zoë on the arm. 'Zo, if I stay here with Martin, would you mind taking Bella sledging?'

'Please, please, please, Zoë!' Bella grabbed hold of Zoë's leg and hung on for dear life. Zoë smiled down at her.

'I'd be delighted. And I promise I'll take very good care of her.'

'I know you will. Thanks, Zo.'

Leaving Martin and Mandy behind, they headed out into the darkness, Zoë hanging onto Bella with one hand and Juliet with the other. As they approached the chairlift, she had a thought.

'How do we get Arnie up there? Is he allowed on the lift?'

'Absolutely not.' Billy looked back and his eyes twinkled in the fairy lights. 'But what they don't know won't hurt them.'

As they reached the bottom of the lift, Billy unzipped his jacket, crouched down, bundled the excited dog into his arms and zipped it up again. Zoë and the others giggled at the sight of two heads peeking out of the collar and a black tail wagging furiously out of the bottom. The lift operator must have noticed, but he gave no sign. Presumably Billy had ensured his compliance.

Zoë made sure she got onto a different chair from Grant. After what Mandy had told her, the further away she stayed from him, the better. It was bitterly cold on the lift, but she had deliberately put on her warmest clothes, and she was fine. She hugged Bella to her, but she too was cocooned in two or three layers of clothing and didn't look in the least bit cold.

At the top, they found the solid wooden sledges waiting for them. Billy released the dog from his jacket and they grinned at the sight of him running round and round in circles, barking excitedly. A helpful lift man lit the flaming torches for them and warned them to avoid letting the burning oily tar drip onto their clothes. He showed them the arms of his old jacket, which looked as if they had been riddled with bullets. Zoë and Juliet exchanged glances – no doubt Health and Safety would have something to say about this had they been back home in the UK.

Juliet went with Billy and Daniela. Zoë and Lorna took Bella, and the other three piled onto the third sledge. The lift man gave them a thirty-second lesson on how to use their feet to steer and brake, and then they were off. At the very first corner, Zoë nearly steered her sledge into a snowdrift, but a lucky kick of her boot at the last moment averted disaster, though only as far as the next bend. All three sledges overturned several times on the way down, the dog almost got run over numerous times, most of the torches went out, and they were all covered in snow but laughing their heads off by the time they finally made it round the last corner and headed down to the bottom of the lift. Here they extinguished the last remaining torches and handed everything back to the lift man.

Just to prove that her balance when not on skis was as bad as ever, Zoë then managed to fall over twice on the hundred-yard walk back to the hotel, and by the time they finally made it into the hall, they were all almost paralytic with laughter. It had indeed been a fun evening. They all went off to change, and Zoë took Bella back along the corridor and tapped on her parents' door. They had to wait for almost a minute before Mandy appeared, wearing one of the hotel bathrobes. She looked a bit flushed and Zoë had a sudden suspicion as to how she and Martin had been spending their time. She caught Mandy's eye and winked, and the flush that spread over her friend's face confirmed her suspicions. This was very good news – as long as Martin hadn't damaged his arm in the process.

Dinner was another excellent meal, this time featuring a wonderful selection of charcoal-grilled meats and a mouth-watering choice of desserts. Afterwards, they retired to the lounge and watched another movie on the big screen. It was almost midnight before Zoë dragged herself to her feet and headed for bed. She was feeling quite tired after the active day, and she wasted no time in getting into bed. She had just put the light out when she heard a tap at the door. Cursing under her breath, she went across to see who it was, knowing full well that if it was Grant, she was going to give him an earful. But it wasn't Grant. Standing there was Lorna, looking apologetic – and confused.

'I'm so sorry, Zo. I know it's late and I can see you've already gone to bed, but I've just had a text and I don't know what to do.'

She really did look worried, so Zoë put sleep on hold for a few minutes and invited her in.

'So what was in the text, Lorn?'

'He says he's already bought his ticket. He's flying over tomorrow and he's booked into a hotel in the village.'

'Well that's his hard luck, isn't it.? You don't need to see him, do you?'

'No, of course not, but he mentioned the ball and I was wondering about maybe inviting him to it. Seeing as he's come so far, it's the least I can do.'

Zoë didn't think this sounded like a very good idea, but she knew the decision wasn't hers to make.

'You do what you think is best, but if it was me, I wouldn't have any more to do with him. On a more positive note, if Prince Charming does turn up at the ball, that means Juliet and I will have him all to ourselves.'

Lorna managed a smile.

'You deserve him, Zo. I think I'll sleep on it and maybe ask Billy in the morning about getting an extra ticket. He was telling me that security's going to be tight as there'll be a number of famous people there.'

'Like Billy himself.'

Lorna nodded. 'It's amazing how he's done so well for himself.' She turned for the door. 'Anyway, thanks, as always, for being a shoulder to cry on.'

'Happy to help.'

Zoë let Lorna out and returned to bed, wondering if she really had helped. Lorna was going to have to work out what to do for herself, and it sounded as though she was going to invite this guy whatever anyone else said. She had only just turned the light out when she heard another tap at the door. Cursing with even more feeling now, she flicked the light back on and stomped across to the door. To her surprise, it was Lorna again.

'Hi again, Lorn. Forget something?'

Lorna glanced surreptitiously over her shoulder and gently pushed her way in, closing the door quietly behind her. Zoë stepped back, wondering what was going on.

'You know you said you'd finally had it out with Grant and told him it was all over?'

'Yes.' Zoë wondered where she was going with this.

'And no regrets?'

Zoë wasn't going to reveal Mandy's secret, so she just nodded. 'None whatsoever. Telling him it's all over is the best thing I've done all year. Why do you ask?'

'I just thought you might be interested to know that as I was closing my door a few seconds ago, I saw Erika from reception sneak down the corridor and tap on Grant's door. A few seconds later, she disappeared inside. I thought I'd tell you just in case you were harbouring any doubts about your decision to jettison Grant. Anyway, I really am going this time. Night, night, Zo.' She kissed Zoë on the cheek and let herself out again.

As Zoë climbed back into bed, she reflected that it was now past midnight, so it was already technically Christmas Eve. Evidently Grant intended marking the anniversary of his desertion of her in typical Grant fashion. She gave a heartfelt sigh and flicked the light off. Any lingering feelings she might still have had for her ex were totally and utterly wiped out now, and she was left with no remorse and a keen sense of relief. Brutal as this last year had been, losing Grant had been the best thing that could have happened to her.

And anyway, she told herself as she drifted off to sleep, who knows who I might meet at the Christmas ball?

Chapter 16

Zoë woke up on Christmas Eve to brilliant sunshine pouring in through a crack in the curtains. A check of the time revealed that it was already eight o'clock – she really had slept well. With no special plans for today, she was able to lie there for a while, thinking back over everything. One way or another, things were working out for everybody. Her talents as an agony aunt were apparently unimpaired even after ten years.

Mandy and Martin would appear to have rediscovered their marital mojo – even if it was at the expense of a broken arm and a bang on the head. Lorna was hopefully heading towards the new less licentious life she had been longing for, and Imogen and Fergus were looking more like a real couple than when they had first arrived. Billy was obviously very happy with Daniela, and Juliet appeared carefree and relaxed.

That just left Grant and herself. As far as Zoë was concerned, Grant's life was now totally his own, and she had no further desire to stay in contact with him. As for herself, she felt relief at having finally cleared away the wreckage of her time with him, but where did that leave her? There was her job and, of course, the ramifications of her refusal to do the *HC* article for Damien. But irrespective of her editor's reaction, she knew she had no intention of spending the rest of her life writing articles about so-called celebrities, so her first task upon returning to London was definitely going to be to start seriously hunting for a new job – maybe with one of the online news organisations. She reached for her phone and checked her emails. Ominously there was still nothing from Damien. She sighed to herself but remained convinced she had acted correctly.

On a more personal note, although she certainly wasn't dead set on finding herself another man, she thought to herself with a smile that if Prince Charming were to pop up tonight at the ball, maybe she'd be prepared to accept his advances. And if he didn't put in an appearance, *tant pis*, as the French would say. She knew there were precious few Prince Charmings about, so she wouldn't be too disappointed. Her smile broadened as she reminded herself that if Lorna did decide to invite her former lover to the ball, that would increase her own chances of finding her prince.

She took her time over getting up and dressed, and it was almost nine o'clock when she arrived in the breakfast room. Mandy and Imogen were in there and both of them were looking like the cats that had got the cream. Bella was sitting beside them, and when she spotted Zoë, she came rushing over to grab hold of her legs and hug her. Zoë looked down with a smile.

'Morning, Bella, and how are you today?'

Bella didn't reply, but the affectionate look she shot upwards almost turned Zoë's legs to jelly. She bent down and kissed the top of the little girl's head. Yes, there was no getting away from it, she wanted a Bella. And that, as Juliet had so rightly remarked, would involve finding a big, smelly – or hopefully not so smelly – man.

Making sure she and her human limpet didn't topple over onto the breakfast buffet, she filled a bowl with fruit salad, ordered an omelette, and shuffled carefully across to join the others, the little girl still hanging onto her.

'Morning, ladies. You're looking fine and happy this morning.'

She glanced around the table and there was no doubt about it. Imogen and Mandy were both exuding what Zoë's sixth sense identified as a post-coital glow, and she felt happy for them.

'It's a beautiful day.' Imogen sounded cheerful. 'And of course it's Christmas tomorrow.'

'Christmas, Christmas!' Bella launched happily into a rendition of 'Jingle Bells' and the adults exchanged glances.

'What time was she awake this morning?' Zoë looked across at Mandy.

'Surprisingly late – presumably because of the sledging and the fresh air last night. But if last Christmas is anything to go by, she'll probably be awake at five tomorrow morning – assuming we manage to get her off to sleep tonight.'

Zoë looked across the room. There were one or two presents already on the floor at the foot of the tree, and she made a mental note to add her own gifts to the pile after she had wrapped them. As her hot chocolate arrived, so did Juliet and Lorna. She wondered what decision Lorna had made about her former boyfriend, but decided not to ask in front of the others.

'Morning, you two. Sleep well?'

Juliet poured a glass of orange juice and came over to them.

'Like a log – in fact I have done every night this week. It must be the mountain air.'

She looked very serene and Zoë wondered yet again to whom she had been referring the other day when she had admitted to feeling attraction to somebody here. She had spent quite a bit of time speculating who it could be, but without success. In any case, now that all the couples looked far more settled – and assuming that there was surely no way Juliet could possibly have designs upon Grant – presumably she had had to lay those feelings to rest. Of course, there was always the unknown quantity of tonight's ball. Mind you, Zoë thought, the chances of there being two Prince Charmings in the same place on the same night – or three if Lorna was also on the lookout – were likely to be slim in the extreme. She smiled at the thought and dedicated herself to her fruit salad.

'So, who's doing what today?' Lorna came across and sat down. By this time, Bella had climbed up onto Zoë's lap and was happily picking the blueberries out of her fruit salad, under the disapproving eyes of her mother.

'The forecast's good if anybody feels like skiing.' Juliet looked across at Zoë. 'Or are you off with Billy again?'

Zoë shook her head. 'It wasn't discussed. I imagine he must have things to do – especially with the ball coming up tonight. Besides, I think it's only fair I let Daniela have her husband back. I've been hogging him a bit.'

'She really doesn't seem bothered, Zo.' Juliet grinned. 'I don't think you need worry about finding yourself with an Italian knife in the back. Anyway, she and I are going for a nice gentle ski this morning. You're very welcome to join us.'

Zoë's omelette arrived at that moment and she picked up her fork.

'I will, thanks. I need to justify having a cooked breakfast. What about the rest of you? Any plans?'

'I promised I'd take Bella skating on the lake this morning – her skiing lessons have finished for Christmas. That way Martin can have a bit of a lie-in.' Mandy grinned. 'For some reason he's feeling rather worn out this morning.'

Ignoring the innuendo – traditionally her prerogative – Lorna explained her own plans for the day.

'I'm taking the train to Salzburg and back. I really loved the look of the place the other night.'

Zoë wondered if this meant Lorna had decided to go and meet her boyfriend off the plane, but made no comment.

'And what about you, Imogen?'

'The usual – rest and recuperation. This holiday has been doing me so much good.'

'And Fergus?'

'He went off snowboarding at eight o'clock. He's a total addict. Still, he was only saying this morning how much happier he feels as a result of this break. We've all got so much to thank Billy for, haven't we? And not just Billy.' As she said it, her eyes met Zoë's, but neither passed comment.

–

Zoë had a lovely morning's skiing with Daniela and Juliet and enjoyed chatting to them while they were on the lifts. She was delighted to see that Juliet had been right. Daniela appeared to be completely relaxed about the fact that her husband had been spending time on the slopes with another woman. In fact, she had a message for Zoë from Billy.

'Billy's had to go to Salzburg again this morning – a business thing – but he asked me to ask if you felt like a quick ski with him this afternoon. He and I have to be back by four at the latest, but he said something about powder skiing again, if you're up for it. He said he'll try and meet us up at the main restaurant at lunchtime.'

That sounded like an excellent idea to Zoë – as long as Billy didn't take her over any more precipices. Yesterday had been amazing, but she still found herself remembering that frighteningly steep first section, and knew she would be happier doing something a little bit less challenging – not least as she would be dancing the night away later.

After a most enjoyable morning on the slopes, they reached the restaurant at half past twelve. They were fortunate to arrive on the terrace just as a group was leaving, and so managed to take over their table. They settled down, basking in the warm sunshine – although in the shade the temperature was still around zero – and ordered sandwiches. As it turned out, Billy didn't arrive until about one o'clock, apologising for his lateness.

'Sorry, Danni, sorry girls, I got held up in Salzburg. Anyway, that's it as far as business is concerned until after Christmas. Had a good morning?'

Daniela nodded and answered for all of them.

'Beautiful. Maybe a bit tame for Zoë, but I told her you would take her off piste this afternoon.'

Billy looked across at Zoë. 'Fancy a bit of powder again?'

'That sounds terrific, but please, no terribly steep slopes. I almost had nightmares last night.'

'Of course. How does an hour or two in the trees sound? No precipices, no *Hubschrauber*, just a pleasant afternoon in the deep snow.'

'That sounds perfect.'

And that was what it turned out to be. As Daniela and Juliet disappeared down the main piste, Zoë set off after Billy through the fir trees. They worked their way gradually across the slope as far as the last lift. This was a long chairlift, and once they were sitting on it, they had a chance to talk.

Zoë filled him in on developments with the other members of the group – without revealing any secrets – and he looked and sounded happy for them all. He then managed to put his finger on the odd one out.

'And what about you, Zoë? Now you say it's all definitely over between you and Grant, what's your next move?'

She grinned at him. 'I'm pinning my hopes on the ball tonight. Like I told you, I'll dig out my glass slippers and hope that Prince Charming puts in an appearance.'

'And if he doesn't?'

'I'm not bothered. With a few exceptions – like yourself, for example – I'm not exactly too keen on the male of the species at the moment. It'll probably take a while, but sooner or later I imagine I'll meet someone, and I'll just have to hope this one's better than the last.'

'You'll meet someone, Zoë. I know it. You're bright, you're very beautiful and you've got a big heart.'

Fortunately they reached the top of the lift at this point, just before Zoë's embarrassment became too obvious. As they set off again across the slope in the other direction, she found herself thinking almost wistfully about Billy. If only she had known him before Daniela. Of course, she corrected herself, she *had* known him before Daniela, but that was back in his nerdy days. And this recent attraction wasn't just because Billy was now immensely rich. It was because he was a truly nice, generous man, who also happened to be very good-looking.

As she followed his dancing form ahead of her, she had to admit that he did have a rather fine backside. Such was her attention to the aesthetic aspects of his derrière, however, her concentration slipped, and for the first time this week, she lost control and went flying, landing in a heap, half buried in a snowdrift.

Gingerly she lifted her head and took stock. She had lost her woolly hat, her hair was covered in snow and she could feel a cold, damp sensation in the open neck of her jacket and even down her back. Her skis had come away from their bindings and were presumably somewhere underneath all the snow, and she had lost both her poles. She struggled into a kneeling position, relieved not to feel any pain – presumably only her pride was injured. As she hunted around for her poles to give her some leverage as she tried to stand up in the deep snow, she heard Billy's voice.

'You okay, Zo?' He sidestepped up to her.

She wiped a handful of snow off her face. 'I'm fine, thanks. No damage done.'

'First time this week, right?'

She wiped more snow off her face and shook her hair to remove the worst of it, reaching inside the neck of her jumper to dislodge a few bits of ice.

'Yup. The Greeks called it hubris – gross overconfidence leading to a tragic downfall. I wasn't concentrating.' She didn't tell him *what* she had been concentrating on.

'Hang on, I'll give you a hand.'

She saw him park his poles and sidestep towards her until he was able to reach down and catch hold of her hands in his. He made it look very easy as he tugged her to her feet. In fact, she came up so quickly, she almost toppled the two of them over, ending up plastered up against him, both of them desperately windmilling their arms to maintain their balance. As they stabilised, she looked up at his face, only a few inches from hers.

'Thanks, Billy. I'm okay now.'

As she spoke, she realised that she was much closer to a married man than she should be, so she stepped back hastily, sinking up to her thighs in soft snow as she did so. He reached down again, but she waved him away.

'Thanks, Billy, but I think I've just put my foot on one of my skis under here.'

Laboriously she retrieved first one ski and then the other. One pole was lying with the skis, but she wasted almost five minutes probing for the other one before finally finding it. As she was doing so, she also found her hat, which was a relief.

All in all, the fall probably held them up for almost a quarter of an hour. When she was finally back on her skis, with her decidedly chilly hat on her head, she apologised to him.

'Sorry about that, Billy. Next time I'll take more care.'

'No need for apologies. Besides, it's an opportunity for me to give you this.'

To her surprise, she saw him pull off a glove and reach into his jacket, bringing out a little square packet wrapped in stripy white and gold paper and tied with a silver bow.

'What's this, Billy? A Christmas present?'

'Here, have a look.' He handed it to her and she took it hesitantly. 'And no, it's not really a Christmas present. I've got some small gifts for you and all the others to go under the tree, but this is just a little something special from me to you. I thought I'd give it to you when we were alone.'

Zoë didn't know what to say. She tugged off her gloves and dropped them in the snow at her feet as she undid the bow and unfolded the wrapping paper to reveal a little black box. Inside, resting on a velvet pad, was the most exquisite thin gold chain and, hanging from it, a tiny pair of golden skis. The label inside the lid said simply *Cartier*. It was delightful and no doubt horrifically expensive. Zoë looked up in awe.

'This is amazing, Billy, but I can't accept it. It's far, far too valuable.'

'Don't worry about that, Zoë. I'd just like you to have it. You've always meant a lot to me. Please take it. It would make me very happy.'

Before she could come up with any kind of reply, he pulled his glove back on, zipped up his jacket, and propelled himself back away from her until he could turn and slip off sideways down the slope. As he went, she heard him shout back over his shoulder, 'Remember to concentrate this time.'

Zoë pushed the box and the wrapping paper into a side pocket of her jacket and zipped it securely. She retrieved her gloves and set off after him, skiing slowly, fully aware that she wasn't concentrating as closely as she should be. Her mind was full of the beautiful necklace and the fact that this was a married man who was giving a secret – and very expensive – gift to a woman who wasn't his wife.

It was a miracle she managed to ski back down in his tracks without another accident. All the time she was turning it over in her head. What was going on? Why had he given her the necklace? What did it mean? Yes, they were good friends, but so were the others. Why single her out for such an extravagant gift? Did he think about her differently from the others? As they drew closer and closer to the bottom, an uncomfortable thought occurred to her. Was his intention for this to lead up to some sort of quid pro quo? Was he expecting her to provide him with something in exchange? For a moment, she was reminded of the callous way Grant had taken advantage of Mandy's moment of weakness. Surely Billy wasn't cut from the same cloth.

By the time they reached the bottom and were skiing towards the hotel, she had decided to give him back the necklace, determined to explain as politely and kindly as possible that she didn't feel right accepting such a gift from a married man. Most probably, she thought to herself, this was just the old naïve Billy not realising that such things simply weren't done. She was composing the right words – desperate to avoid hurting or insulting him – as she drew up alongside him, but then saw that they weren't going to be alone. As she came to a halt, Daniela and Juliet also arrived down the slope, reaching the gate to the hotel at the same time.

Daniela leant over and kissed her husband affectionately on the cheek.

'*Ciao*, Billy.'

'*Ciao*, Danni. Had a good afternoon? And you, Juliet?'

'Lovely, thanks. It's been a super day altogether.'

'Right then.' Billy released his bindings and bent down to pick up his skis. 'Now I've got to fly. The dance starts at eight and I've got all sorts of stuff to do first. I thought we could maybe all meet up in our lounge at seven thirty or so for a few nibbles and a glass of champagne before turning up at the dance fashionably late. Thanks again for the company, Zoë. Hope you aren't too knocked about.'

As he hurried off, Juliet caught hold of Zoë's arm.

'Knocked about? Have you had a fall, Zo? You're looking a bit dopey. You didn't hit your head or anything, did you?'

Zoë shook her head – partly to say no and partly to clear the thoughts still swirling about.

'No, I'm absolutely fine. I took a nosedive into a snowdrift, but luckily there weren't any rocks about. What you see is just my normal dopiness.'

Chapter 17

When Zoë got back to her room, the first thing she did was to check her emails. Once again, there was nothing from Damien. Of course, she told herself, it was Christmas Eve, but then, in the same breath, she remembered that nobody in the office could ever remember him having a holiday – or even a day off. She closed the laptop and did her best not to think about the rocket she was almost certainly going to receive from him.

After a little doze on the bed, she took a long hot bath before putting on the lovely fluffy bathrobe and concentrating on wrapping all the little presents she had bought for the others. It was fortunate that this wasn't a complicated job, as her mind was still on the necklace. She hadn't said anything to Billy in the presence of his wife about returning the gift, but she knew that she would have to give it back to him at the earliest opportunity. One thing was for sure – she was never, ever going to let herself become the Other Woman, responsible for destroying somebody else's marriage. The only question was when she was likely to get him on his own. If all else failed, she felt pretty sure he would be asking her to go skiing with him again sometime over the next couple of days, so she carefully put the box back into its paper and zipped it securely in the pocket of her skiing jacket. She could pick her moment when they were out on the slopes, away from prying eyes and ears.

When she had finished wrapping all the presents, she piled them on the sofa. They had agreed that presents would be put under the tree in the lounge later that night, after Bella had gone to bed. Martin had warned his daughter that Santa was making a special journey all the way from Britain to Austria, so she knew her presents wouldn't arrive until the middle of the night. Zoë had bought her a gorgeous teddy bear, sporting a traditional Austrian jacket and jaunty hat with a feather in it. Wrapping it hadn't been easy, but she felt pretty confident that the little girl would like it. She knew that five-year-old Zoë would have loved it. In fact, thirty-two-year-old Zoë definitely liked it a lot.

She took a good deal of care getting dressed. It was pretty clear that the Christmas ball was going to be a very smart affair. Although she wasn't dressing up to impress anybody in particular – unless, of course, Prince Charming managed to put in an appearance – she felt she owed it to Billy and Daniela to try to look her best. She spent an age making sure that her hair was pinned up as perfectly as possible. Fortunately this task was greatly helped by the Hotel Schlossberg having thoughtfully provided a clever mirror system in the bathroom that allowed her to see what she was doing to the back of her head. It took her a long time, but when she finally stood in front of the mirror to survey the results of her efforts, she was pretty satisfied with her appearance. A few days of serious exercise and lots of fresh air had given her face a healthy glow, and the unpolluted mountain air meant that her eyes were clear, the blue-grey of the irises standing out crisply against the white surrounds.

She checked the time and saw to her surprise that it was already well past seven. She slipped into the new silk dress, stepped into her heels and took a long hard look at herself in the full-length mirror on the wardrobe door. The plunging neckline was a bit more revealing than she was used to, but after leaning forward and back and hunching her shoulders, she felt confident that she was structurally sound. As a final touch, she dug out the silver necklace with the little pine marten and clipped it around her neck. The silver went well with the blue-grey of the dress and with her eyes. She would do.

She made her way through to the lounge and found that she wasn't the first. Lorna had beaten her to it.

'Hi, Lorn. Did you have a good time in Salzburg?'

Lorna nodded before coming over and speaking quietly into Zoë's ear, even though they were the only people in the lounge for the moment.

'Salzburg was lovely. I decided this morning that although I won't be sharing a bed with anybody tonight, I should at least get an invitation to the ball for you-know-who.'

'And did you?'

'Yes. Billy actually gave me a lift down to Salzburg in his gorgeous car. I told him the whole story – just like I told you – and he gave me an invitation.' She hesitated. 'Although he said pretty much the same thing you did. Anyway, me being me, I didn't listen to either of you, and now I'm beginning to wish I had.'

'Like I said, it's your decision.' Zoë still thought Lorna would have done better to sever all ties, but decided there was nothing to be gained by commenting after the event. 'I look forward to meeting your man.'

'He's definitely not my man.' Lorna gripped Zoë's arm and leant even closer. 'I went and met him at the airport, and as soon as I saw him again, it all came back with a rush. He and I really used to do some pretty tacky things, and I'm over that now. However, from the propositions he was making to me in the train on the way back here, he appears to have got even worse. The trouble is, by that time I'd given him the invitation, so I'm just going to have to put up with him this evening.'

Zoë gave her a sympathetic smile. 'Doesn't sound like the gala ball's going to be a bundle of laughs for you, then.'

Lorna nodded morosely. 'I should have taken your advice, Zoë. I should have known.' There was the sound of voices at the door, so she hastily whispered a few last words before changing the subject. 'Auntie Zoë always knows best.'

'I'm not so sure about that.'

As the door opened and Juliet appeared, Lorna raised her voice to normal pitch once more. 'Wow, Jules, that's a stunning dress you're wearing.'

'Thanks, Lorn. You're looking super as well.'

Zoë agreed. Lorna really was looking lovely in an uncharacteristically conservative and classy black gown. Juliet herself was wearing the dress she had bought back in London in the Black Friday sales. Her choice was cream in colour, with an open back, and it fitted her perfectly. She too had put her hair up. She looked great and Zoë nodded admiringly.

'Jules, you look gorgeous too. If Prince Charming does turn up, I won't stand a chance.'

'You've got to be joking, Zo. You look like you've come out of the pages of your own magazine. Hollywood royalty at the very least.'

'Champagne, Fräulein?'

Zoë looked up to see Marcel holding a tray. She gave him a big smile and helped herself to a glass. As she did so, there was a thump as the door was nosed open and Arnie the Labrador came charging in, followed by Billy.

'Arnie, no jumping up!'

Zoë crouched down to ruffle the excited pup's ears, rather pleased that her long skirt covered and protected her good shoes.

'Hi, Arnie. Are you coming to the ball as well, or are you going to be left behind like Cinderella?'

'Arnie's just had a long walk and he'll be fine. This dog has an infinite capacity for sleep, as well as food.' Billy smiled indulgently at the dog. 'I'll take him for a walk before I go to bed, so he can't complain.'

Billy stepped back and surveyed the three girls appreciatively. As ever, he still looked a bit shyer than your average billionaire, as though being in the presence of women in ball gowns was taking him out of his comfort zone. Seeing him like this made his gift all the more confusing to Zoë. Surely it couldn't be a prelude to some sort of indecent proposal. Could it? If he was a wolf in sheep's clothing, it was a brilliant disguise.

'You're all looking wonderful.' He accepted a glass of champagne from Marcel and toasted them unexpectedly formally. 'I hope you all have a most enjoyable night. Cheers.'

As Zoë took a sip of champagne, she checked him out. He was wearing a dinner jacket, and unlike so many men on these formal occasions, he looked as if he was used to wearing it. The jacket was a perfect fit and it suited him down to the ground. Presumably a tux was an essential item in the wardrobe of the CEO of a multi-national company. Yes, she had to admit that he was a very good-looking man. She found herself wondering if he gave presents to other women. With a job like his, and looking like he did, she felt sure there would be no shortage of eager recipients, in spite of his reticent manner. Shaking the thought from her mind, she helped herself to a delicious canapé from another tray, this one brought round by Erika. Stifling any thought of Grant, Zoë summoned a smile.

'*Danke schön, Erika.*'

'*Bitte schön.*'

'Arnie, Arnie!'

The door flew open as Bella came running in, and the dog rushed to greet her and her parents, who appeared in her wake. Martin had chosen a smart dark suit, against which his sling looked a little incongruous. Beside him, Mandy was wearing a long dress with, unusually for her, quite a revealing neckline – not quite up to Lorna's former standard, but nevertheless bold. From the broad Cheshire Cat grin on Martin's face, he approved. Zoë was delighted for both of them. Seconds later, Imogen and Fergus appeared, followed by Grant. He too was wearing a suit – a real rarity for him – and he looked predictably uncomfortable in it. Imogen, on the other hand, was looking very elegant, but all eyes – even the dog's – were on her husband.

'Wow, Fergus. Great pair of knees.' Lorna was impressed. 'There's something about a man in a kilt.'

Zoë giggled, although in fact he looked rather fine in a dark blue and green tartan kilt, black jacket with silver buttons, bow tie, white knee socks and sporran.

'If it's true what they say about kilts, you'd better not go outside, Fergie.' Grant had a broad grin on his face. 'It's really cold now. You could lose those nearest and dearest to you.'

Imogen gave him one of her looks. 'I can assure you, Grant, that I would never allow my husband to go out without appropriate undergarments.'

Bella was dressed in a pink check party frock and her mum had pinned her hair up and added some tinsel to it. The little girl was evidently very excited at the prospect of going to the ball with the grown-ups, although her mother informed Zoë that she wouldn't be staying to the end. Bedtime would be at ten o'clock.

'So does that mean you and Martin will have to leave the dance early?'

Mandy shook her head. 'Not entirely. We're going to take turns at babysitting.'

Zoë had a thought. 'I'd be very happy to help out if you like. A bit of a rest and the chance to take these high heels off partway through the evening sounds like a wonderful idea.'

'Me too. Add me to the rota.' Juliet arrived with a plate of delicious blinis topped with sour cream and caviar. As she handed it round, Zoë spotted the expression on the dog's face. He had plonked himself at her feet and was gazing up in rapt adoration, not at her, but at the underside of the plate of food that his nose had instantly identified. As Bella hesitantly took one of the little canapés and nibbled it suspiciously, Zoë had a feeling that this might prove to be the Labrador's lucky night.

'Well thanks, girls. If you really don't mind, I'm sure Bella will be delighted to have such elegant babysitters.'

Mandy sounded delighted to have a bit of help and Zoë was definitely looking forward to spending more time with the little girl. There was no getting away from it – she was definitely developing unexpected maternal instincts.

They all took the lift down to the ground floor at just after half past eight. As the doors opened, they could hear the music, which got steadily louder as they walked through to the ballroom. To everybody's surprise, it soon became clear that the source of the music was none other than a traditional oompah band. As they opened the doors and made their way into the ballroom, they saw it in full swing. There were four musicians – three older men, and a girl in a frilly dirndl with long blonde plaits sticking out of her Santa Claus hat. The men were wearing leder-hosen with tinsel attached to their braces. She was playing an accordion, while the three men's instruments were a massive shiny brass tuba, a trombone and a trumpet. The resulting sound was very rhythmic and unquestionably Germanic. It was also very, very loud.

Mandy and Martin took Bella out onto the dance floor and did their best to join in with twenty or thirty guests, some of whom appeared to know what they were doing and were prancing about slapping their thighs vigor-ously. As Zoë described it to her mother on the phone next morning, watching them was like watching Morris dancers performing in a Wagnerian opera. She took a good look round. There were probably almost a hundred people in the room already – most standing at the edges clapping, or sitting at tables strategically positioned round the dance floor. She followed Imogen and Fergus to a free table and took a seat. Billy, no doubt in his role as host, had disappeared somewhere, although Daniela was standing chatting to Juliet close to the next table, where Lorna and Grant had already sat down.

Imogen disappeared back to her room to dump her clutch bag, leaving Fergus and Zoë sitting and looking on. After a few seconds, Fergus leant towards Zoë and lowered his voice until it was just audible over the noise of the band.

'Zoë, I gather you've definitely finished with Grant. Is that right?'

'Yes. All over now and I've told him so.'

'Well seeing as it is, there's something I've been wanting to get off my chest. I've got a guilty conscience.'

Zoë gave him a curious look. 'Really?'

He nodded, looking quite ashamed. 'You know the other day – the day of the snowstorm and the white-out?' She nodded. 'Well, it was all a put-up job, a charade.'

'All what was a charade?'

'Grant falling over and us getting lost. He deliberately stopped as we were coming down through the woods and let Erika ski off ahead of us, thinking we'd got lost – or worse. He made me promise not to breathe a word to you, but now that you're definitely broken up, you need to know the truth. To be quite honest, I didn't want anything to do with it, but he pretty much presented me with a fait accompli.'

Zoë was still trying to take in the implications of what she had just heard.

'But why? Why put the emergency services to the trouble of going out in a snowstorm to look for you both, and why let us all get worried? Erika was in a right state.'

'That was the whole point, Zoë – Grant *wanted* you to be worried. The idea was, if you were worried on his behalf, it might make you realise you still had feelings for him.'

'Oh, dear God.' Zoë was appalled. Grant's selfishness knew no bounds. 'I just can't believe even he'd do something so stupid.'

She sat in silence watching the antics on the dance floor for a few moments before turning back towards Fergus.

'Well thanks a lot, Fergus, for coming clean. I don't blame you for your part in the deception. Grant can be very persuasive when he wants to be. In a way, it's just more proof that my decision was the right one.' She smiled as a thought struck her and she lowered her voice, even though there was nobody close by. 'Mind you, somehow I get the impression that that moment when Imogen thought she might have lost you didn't do any harm to *your* relationship.'

Fergus smiled back. 'You're right. That's the other thing I've been meaning to say, Zoë. Imogen told me you gave her some good advice the other day. I can see now why everybody used to come to you for help when you were at university. From what she told me, you made her come to her senses about a lot of things – particularly our relationship. Thanks a lot. I owe you.'

Zoë gave him a smile. She liked this big, friendly Scot. 'You're very welcome, Fergus. I wish you both all the very best for the future.' And she leant closer and kissed him on the cheek.

'Fergus, I leave you alone for one second and the next thing I know, you're in the arms of another woman!'

Imogen reappeared, a bright smile on her face. There was no missing the fact that she was looking and sounding a lot more relaxed and happy now.

Fergus stood up and held out his hand to his wife. 'I'm glad you're back. I was just thinking how this song they're playing reminds me of the Gay Gordons. I feel the urge to dance.'

Imogen rolled her eyes theatrically at Zoë. 'My mother told me not to trust anybody from north of the border, but would I listen? Look what I've got myself into now.'

Nevertheless, she went off smiling and she and Fergus were soon giving a creditable rendition of Scottish dancing to the appreciative crowd – even if Zoë couldn't discern the slightest hint of similarity in the music to any Scottish folk song she had ever heard.

Zoë got up and joined Juliet and Daniela as they clapped their encouragement. Before long, a decent crowd had formed. Suddenly she heard a voice at her ear.

'I'm not a real Scot, but I've got Scottish blood, and I've always wanted to try Scottish dancing. Would you care to join me?'

His accent was unmistakably American. Zoë turned towards him and looked up at his face – and it was a long way up. The man was a giant. He wasn't fat by any means, but there was a lot of him. He sounded pleasant, and there was a friendly smile on his bearded face, but if this was Prince Charming, he had almost certainly been on steroids. Zoë grinned back at him.

'I haven't done Scottish dancing since I was a teenager, but what the hell? Yes, I'd love to.'

His smile broadened. 'Well thank you. My name's Max, by the way.'

'And I'm Zoë. Pleased to meet you, Max.'

The next half-hour was hilarious. Zoë positioned herself as close as possible to Fergus, so she and Max could watch and try to imitate what he did, but there was always a few seconds' satellite delay between his steps and their attempts. To the onlookers – and there were quite a few by this time – it must have looked bizarre, but they were soon joined by an assortment of other guests, most with even less idea of what they should be doing.

By this time, the band had realised that there was now Celtic competition among the revellers and the accordion player even managed a creditable version of something approaching 'Scotland the Brave'. As this finished, she and the trumpet player relinquished their instruments and began to give a sort of Teutonic dancing tutorial, and the guests all did their best to follow suit, slapping their thighs and prancing about with hoots and cries.

Finally Max leant in close to Zoë's ear. 'I think it's time for a sit-down before I have a coronary. Can I buy you a drink?'

Zoë led him back to her table, where a bottle of Sekt in an ice bucket had appeared along with half a dozen glasses. They sat down and moments later were joined by Juliet, looking flushed and happy.

'Hi, Zo. I haven't laughed so much for ages.'

'Max and I were just saying the same thing. This is Max, by the way. Max, this is Juliet.'

'Hi, Juliet. Glass of fizz?' He lifted the heavy bottle out of the bucket with minimal effort and filled three glasses. 'So, are you both guests here at the hotel?'

'Yes. Isn't it a marvellous place?'

'It sure is.'

'Are you staying here too?'

He shook his head. 'No, I live down the road in Salzburg. I know the owner.'

Zoë looked up. 'You know Billy? So do we. We were both at university with him.'

A smile of comprehension spread across Max's face. 'Got it. So you're the famous Zoë.'

Zoë found herself blushing. 'Famous, me? I think you've got me confused with somebody else.'

He shook his head again. 'Nope, no confusion. I spend a lot of time with Billy and he's told me all about you.' He hesitated before adding, 'He's really been looking forward to seeing you all.'

Zoë was puzzled. 'So how do *you* know Billy, Max?'

'I work for him. I'm head of production at WF. He designs the computers. My guys build them. I usually work out of LA, but I've been here for a few months, getting the European production line up and running. I like it so much, I might even set up home over here'

'Hi, girls. I see you've met Big Max.' Zoë looked up to see Billy, with Daniela hanging on his arm. 'I saw you dancing earlier, Max – if that's the word for it. Would a mixture of Austrian and Scottish be termed *McTanzmusik*, I wonder?'

'I don't know what you call it, but it was damn hard work.' Max stood up and gave Daniela a kiss on the cheek. 'Hi there, Danni. Enjoying the dance?'

Daniela smiled back at him. 'Definitely – although maybe not as much as you, Max. You were on fire out there.'

At that moment, the band finally stopped and the silence that ensued was wonderful – but it didn't last long. As the oompah people trooped off the stage to a tumult of applause, the lights dimmed and a single light illuminated a DJ dressed as Father Christmas behind a battery of disco equipment. Seconds later, 'Jailhouse Rock' by none other than the King himself echoed out, and people started flocking back to the dance floor. Max glanced across at Billy.

'Mind if I ask Danni for a dance?'

'Be my guest. I'm going to have to go off and play the gracious host anyway.' Billy smiled at Daniela. 'Word of warning – stay clear of his feet. He stepped on Arnie the other day.'

'I told you it wasn't my fault, and I've got witnesses.' Max grinned at Daniela. 'As long as you don't try to eat my shoes, you'll be fine.' He led her out onto the dance floor, where he stood out a good foot above almost everybody else.

'What a nice guy.' Zoë looked up at Billy. 'You two seem to get on very well together.'

'I've known Big Max since before I went to university. He's the closest thing to a brother I've got.'

'How brilliant to work with somebody you really like. So did you say you'd got to go and be sociable?'

Billy gave her a nod and a wry smile. 'I've just heard that the contingent from Vienna has arrived.'

'Who's come all the way from Vienna?'

'Two cabinet ministers and a celebrity chef, apparently.' He shrugged his shoulders helplessly. 'My PA sent out the invites. Apart from you guys and the guests at the hotel, I don't really know who's been invited.' His smile broadened to a grin. 'Although I do know she sent an invite to Arnie's namesake, but he couldn't make it this time.'

'You know Schwarzenegger?'

'I've met him a few times now. He's been here to Bad Bergstein twice. He's still very Austrian. But he's staying in the States this Christmas.'

'Do you know lots of celebrities?' Zoë was fascinated.

'I get invited to all sorts of events – mostly charity do's to raise money for good causes. In the course of them I've met quite a few of the great and the good – and a fair few of the not so great and good.'

Zoë exchanged glances with Juliet. Computer Billy really had come up in the world.

Billy glanced at his watch and then looked back at Juliet and Zoë. 'Would either of you girls feel like a quick dance before I go off and do my duty? Jules?'

Juliet swallowed her champagne and followed Billy out onto the dance floor. Zoë was watching them – surprised to see that William Fischer, the artist formerly known as Computer Billy, the nerd, was a surprisingly good dancer – when she felt a touch on her shoulder. She looked up. It was Grant.

'Feel like dancing, Zoë?'

She took a deep breath. 'Yes, I do, Grant, but not with you.' Seeing the expression on his face, she explained, 'I've been talking to Mandy. Now why don't you go and bother some other unsuspecting girl? Or maybe Erika's here.'

His face fell, and for just about the first time ever, Zoë saw what could have been an expression of remorse. If it was, it was a positive sign of personal development. She allowed her expression and her tone to soften a fraction.

'It's over, Grant. It was good while it lasted, but I've moved on and you need to do the same.'

'So is it Billy, then?'

'Billy? What do you mean?'

'I saw you looking at him, and you know he fancies the pants off you.'

'He does no such thing.' Zoë could feel her cheeks reddening. 'And I'm certainly not getting involved with a married man. Marital infidelity's your speciality, Grant, not mine. Now go and bother somebody else.'

'Suit yourself. See you round, Zoë.' He ambled off, leaving her even more puzzled.

She glanced across towards the next table and saw a man in a dark jacket sitting opposite Lorna. His back was towards Zoë, but presumably he was Lorna's former lover. The expression on Lorna's face was far from welcoming. Clearly whatever relationship these two had enjoyed in the past, it was now consigned to the annals of history, and anybody could see she was regretting inviting him to the ball. Zoë was delighted to note a suitably chaste distance between the two of them, and out of idle curiosity she got up and went across to see what a man who enjoyed swingers' parties looked like.

'Hi, Lorn, I see you've got company. Hi, I'm Zoë. Pleased to meet you.' She braced herself and looked down at the man. As she did so, he glanced up and grinned.

'Zoë? Wow, you're looking gorgeous, sweetheart.'

Zoë felt her mouth gape and her eyes open wide. Surely not…?

'Do you two know each other, Ron?' Lorna looked as surprised as Zoë felt.

'Yeah, we work together. She writes the words, I take the pictures. Fancy you being here, Zoë, eh?' The wink he gave her left no doubt in Zoë's mind as to what was going on. She had been stupid enough to tell Damien about the ball, and when she had informed him in her last email that she wasn't going to go through with it and wouldn't write the article, he had obviously sent Ron over to dig up as much dirt and take as many photos as possible. The fact that Ron happened to know Lorna had provided an easy way to get an invitation after Zoë's refusal to cooperate. One way or another, Damien had been determined to get his scoop.

'So you're here on business?' Lorna kept her eyes on the photographer, a stunned expression on her face.

'Yeah, sweetheart, just like Zoë.'

'Like Zoë?' Now Lorna's puzzled gaze transferred itself back to Zoë, who was quick to explain.

'No, Ron, not like Zoë. I'm here on holiday – period.' She added a few words of explanation to Lorna. 'My editor asked me to see if I could do an interview with Billy, but I told him no.' She turned back to Ron. 'That's why he sent you, isn't it?'

'Something like that. So where is the great man, anyway? I haven't seen hide nor hair of him yet. And here's me with my spy camera as well.' He tapped a barely discernible lump in the breast pocket of his jacket.

Zoë and Lorna exchanged glances for a second before Lorna stood up.

'If you would both excuse me for a moment.' She stalked off, leaving Ron to his large glass of what looked like neat whisky. He took a hefty pull at it and then looked up at Zoë.

'You realise you're in deep shit back home, don't you?'

Zoë made no response, so he elaborated.

'Damien's hopping mad. The last thing I heard, he was talking about firing you.'

'Let him. I'm not going to betray a friend's trust just so I can get a company car.'

Ron shrugged. 'Suit yourself, but I thought I'd tell you. Anyway, if he does sack you, I can always get you some modelling work.' He tapped the side of his nose with his finger, and Zoë turned on her heel and left before she either threw up or clobbered him.

She walked off around the dance floor to the other side, anxious to put as much distance between herself and Ron as possible. The tempo had slowed as the DJ played Frank Sinatra's 'Have Yourself a Merry Little Christmas', the dancing couples swaying together in time with the music. As she walked, she saw Fergus and Imogen clutching each other tight. She felt mixed emotions – on the one hand she was genuinely pleased for them, but at the same time it made her realise how alone she now was.

She took her time walking round the room, doing her best to regain some semblance of the festive spirit before heading back to her table, where she found Mandy and Bella. The time according to the clock on the wall was well past ten by now, and Mandy was trying to persuade a sleepy Bella that bedtime had arrived. Keen to get away from Ron, Zoë volunteered to take her up. Bella clearly approved.

'Please, please, please can Zoë take me up to bed and tell me a story? Please, please, Mummy, can she?'

Mandy caught Zoë's eye. 'Well if you're sure, that would be ever so kind. I'll come up in half an hour to take over.'

'No rush, Mand. Come at eleven, or send Juliet. You and Martin stay and enjoy yourselves.'

'Don't *you* want to stay? Aren't you having a good time, Zo?'

The answer was no, not really. Irrespective of the arrival of the photographer, Zoë had been thinking along these lines for a while now. The Christmas lights were twinkling, the baubles strung around the room were sparkling, and everybody looked happy. She should have been having a wonderful time as well, but there was no point kidding herself. Something, or someone, was missing. Christmas was almost here – and Christmas, more than any other time of year, was for families, for couples.

And she was here alone.

For just about the first time since arriving in Austria, she found herself feeling a bit down. Not really unhappy, just slightly forlorn, here in the middle of other people's happiness. And the fact that Ron had just confirmed her fears that she would probably find herself out of a job when she returned to London did nothing to lighten her mood. However, determined not to show weakness, she rallied and produced a smile.

'No, I'm fine, Mand. It's just a bit hot, that's all. I need to cool down.'

She saw that Mandy wasn't convinced, but after a bit she agreed to let Zoë take over. 'Well if you're sure, that's terrific. Here's the key to the room. Now Bella, you be a good girl and remember to clean your teeth. I'll be up a bit later on.' She bent down and kissed her daughter's cheek. 'Goodnight, sweetie.'

The little girl threw her arms around her mother and hugged her. As she did so, Zoë felt a distinct tug at the heartstrings. There was no getting away from it – she wanted one of these.

'Night, night, Mummy. I love you.'

Zoë took Bella's hand and they turned to leave. As they did so, Lorna reappeared at the next table, accompanied by two large men in dark blue suits. As Zoë and the little girl walked past, she saw Ron being dragged unceremoniously out of the room. She spared a thought for Lorna, who had just discovered – not for the first time in her life – that a man had taken advantage of her. She resolved to sit down with her as soon as Mandy relieved her from her babysitting duty.

Zoë and Bella took the lift up to the top floor and walked along the corridor to Martin and Mandy's room. Unsurprisingly, the reception desk up there wasn't manned and Zoë wondered for a moment whether Erika would make an appearance in Grant's bed later on. No sooner had the thought crossed her mind than she shook it away impatiently. Grant was well and truly out of her life now.

She supervised Bella's trip to the bathroom and her change into pyjamas, listening to the non-stop chatter from the excited little girl about all the presents she was hoping Santa Claus would bring. Once she was safely settled down, with just the bathroom light shedding light into the room, Zoë took a seat alongside the bed. No sooner had she sat down than a little voice came from under the covers.

'Tell me a story, Zoë… please.'

'What sort of story? Have you got a book somewhere?'

'I know all the stories in the books. Can't you just make one up? Please, please, please?'

'All right, I'll do my best, but it won't be as good as your normal stories.'

Zoë settled back in her chair and did a bit of thinking. She had never been asked to make up a bedtime story before, so she took refuge in dim memories from her own childhood.

'Do you know the story of the Ugly Duckling?'

'Sort of…'

'Well, you see, there once was an Ugly Duckling. He lived beside a lake with the rest of his family. He had six brothers and sisters and they were all a lovely soft fluffy yellow colour, while he was a dirty grey colour.'

'Why was he dirty grey?'

'Shh, you just try to go to sleep and I'll explain.'

Zoë carried on with her tale, realising that just about all she remembered of the story was that the ugly duckling turned into a beautiful swan at some stage. As Bella had been skating on the frozen lake that morning, she set the story here in Bad Bergstein, adding a number of familiar characters, such as Georg the waiter, Big Max, and Arnie the dog. As Bella's eyes closed, the story came ever closer to home. The Ugly Duckling's father slipped and broke his wing, but he got better, and the ducklings all ended up at a grand ball given by the handsome Prince Charming. It was while describing events at the ball that everything got a bit confused and the Ugly Duckling ended up turning into Prince Charming. Fortunately, though, by this point

Bella had fallen fast asleep and Zoë let her voice drop to a whisper and then fade out.

Silence descended upon the room. She leant back and relaxed, revisiting in her head the sensations she had felt down in the ballroom. There was no getting away from it – the sight of all these happy people in their family groups had stirred a feeling of loneliness in her. Prince Charming hadn't shown up at the Ball, so sooner or later, she would have to start looking, or face the prospect that so haunted Lorna – growing old alone. She sighed to herself.

And as if that weren't enough, it now looked pretty certain that her return to London would mean unemployment – or at the very least a serious dressing-down by her boss and a big setback to her career. She knew she had done the right thing, but the thought of what was to come further served to dampen her spirits.

Her introspection was interrupted by a quiet knock at the door. She tiptoed across and opened it to find Mandy outside.

'Did she behave herself? Is she asleep?'

'Yes to both. I told her a story and she fell asleep before I got to the end – which is just as well as I'm not sure I knew how it was going to end.'

Mandy came into the room. 'What was the story about?'

'Sort of a cross between the Ugly Duckling and Prince Charming.'

A smile spread across Mandy's face. 'I think we both know who that is, don't we?'

'Do we?'

Mandy nodded. 'Think about it.' She grinned. 'Now listen, I'm desperate to go to the loo, so you get off and enjoy the rest of the night. Thank you so much, Zo… for everything.' She kissed Zoë on the cheek and pushed her gently out of the room.

Chapter 18

When Zoë got back downstairs, the oompah band had just reached the end of their last set and the DJ was playing a slow number. Couples were swaying about and to Zoë's surprise and delight, in the midst of them she spotted Lorna, enveloped in the massive arms of none other than Big Max. They both looked happy and Zoë's spirits rose at the sight of them together.

She took a seat alongside Juliet and pointed them out.

'I see Lorna's found a replacement for her photographer friend.'

'Yes, she got him thrown out. Apparently he was a paparazzo, sent to spy on Billy.'

'I don't know about paparazzo – to me he's just a scumbag.'

'She said you knew him. How come he pitched up here?'

'It's my fault, I'm afraid.'

As they were on their own, Zoë went on to tell her the whole sad story. Juliet heard her out before passing judgement.

'You don't have anything to reproach yourself for. It's not as if you invited him.'

'I just shouldn't have told anyone at work where I was spending Christmas.'

'Forget it. There's no harm done. And you've told your editor you're not doing the article about Billy, so that's fine. As for Lorna, the way she and Max are getting on, you never know, she may have found her Prince Charming after all.'

Zoë smiled. 'Max is a really nice guy. Sort of a benevolent giant – not like the one in Jack and the Beanstalk.'

Juliet smiled back. 'Have you been telling Bella fairy stories?'

'Yes, but it wasn't that one. The only one I could sort of remember was the story of the Ugly Duckling.'

'Well we all know who that is, don't we?'

'We do?'

'Just think about it, Zo.'

Zoë was reflecting when she felt a touch on her bare shoulder.

'Hi, Zoë. I gather you've been doing your Mary Poppins act. All well with Bella?'

She looked up to see Billy smiling down at her.

'She's fast asleep. Mandy's with her now.'

'I'll give her half an hour and then I'll go up and relieve her.' Juliet pointed across the room. 'Martin appears to be having fun on the dance floor with Danni – even with his arm in a sling – but I'm sure he'd like a last dance or two with his wife before going to bed.' She glanced up at Billy. 'Come and sit down. You've been rushing around all night.'

Billy sat down gratefully opposite them and rested his elbows on the tabletop. He looked as if he was feeling a bit tired, but then, Zoë thought to herself, so was she. She wondered if she should say something about the Ron incident, but decided to leave it to a quieter moment. That way she would be able to explain the whole thing to him properly, and she owed it to him to do so. She yawned, checked the clock on the wall, and saw that it was only just past eleven, but the mountain air was taking its toll. At that moment, a waitress came past with a tray and Billy grabbed three glasses of Sekt off it.

'Cheers, girls, and thanks so much for coming. Seeing you all again has made my year.'

As Zoë raised her glass and clinked it against his, she added her own thanks.

'We're the ones who should be doing the thanking. You've got a fabulous place here and you've been so very generous.' She felt her expression grow more serious. 'This year's been pretty terrible for me, and this week has been just the tonic I needed. And, more importantly, it's finally provided me with closure on the whole sad Grant saga.'

Juliet reached over and took her hand. 'Of course, it was exactly one year ago, wasn't it?'

Zoë nodded. 'Yup. This time last year I thought my world had ended. I cried and cried and cried. It's taken time, but I've discovered that the world keeps on turning after all, and now finally – thanks to Billy – the future looks a whole lot brighter.'

Billy took hold of her other hand. 'If I've been able to help in any way, Zoë, I'm glad. Your happiness means a lot to me.'

At that moment Daniela reappeared, followed by Martin. Zoë pulled her hand away from Billy's and looked up at them.

'Hi, you two. You look hot.'

As they both collapsed into chairs, Daniela replied, 'I'm worn out. I haven't danced so much for months, years.'

'So you don't feel like coming for a dance with me now?' Billy pushed his glass across to her. 'Here, have a drink.'

'Thanks, Billy, but I've drunk enough wine tonight – and I'm certainly too exhausted to think about dancing for a bit. In fact I know exactly what I'm going to do. I'm going to go and get myself a big glass of water. Dance with somebody else. Zoë looks the freshest of the bunch. Zoë, go and dance with my husband, would you?'

As Danni got to her feet and set off in search of water, Billy looked across the table at Zoë again.

'Fancy it, Zoë? You're not too tired, are you?'

For a moment Zoë thought about taking refuge in tiredness, but then decided that as it had been Billy's wife who had suggested they dance, she couldn't be harbouring any feelings of jealousy, so she smiled back at him and nodded.

'I'd be delighted, Billy.'

They went out onto the dance floor and she was soon enjoying herself. It gradually dawned on her that here she was, in the middle of happy, smiling people, and she wasn't on her own. All right, she only had Billy on loan for a few minutes, but it felt great to be dancing with a good guy – even if he was already spoken for.

After a while, the music slowed and Billy caught hold of her, pulling her close. She felt his hands on her waist and she reached up, placing her arms loosely around his neck. As the music played, she rocked gently against him, and a feeling of belonging and happiness spread through her. Now that the Grant business was finally laid to rest, she was really pleased to be here, and she owed Billy a lot. She raised her eyes and saw him looking down at her. She smiled up at him, and he smiled back.

'I'm glad to see you looking happy, Zoë. Really pleased.'

'I am, Billy, and it's down to you.'

'Like I said before, your happiness means a lot to me.' He looked and sounded as if he meant it.

There was something in his tone that reminded her she had to talk to him about the necklace. They were hardly in private here, but she took a stab at it anyway.

'Billy, I've been meaning to talk to you. It's about the necklace – that lovely necklace you gave me. You do understand why I can't accept it, don't you?'

Seeing a strange expression in his eyes, she did her best to explain without hurting his feelings.

'Something like that's a very special, very intimate gift. It's terribly generous of you, but it's not the sort of thing I could possibly accept from you. You must understand, surely? You're a married man now, Billy, and you're not like Grant. You're a good guy, and good guys don't give gorgeous gold necklaces to girls who aren't their wives. You do get that, don't you?'

To her surprise, she saw him smile, and she definitely felt his arms tighten a little around her waist.

'Zoë, you're a wonderful girl. How on earth did you end up with somebody like Grant?'

'I've spent twelve months asking myself that, Billy. Love's a funny thing.'

He nodded, his head almost touching hers as he did so. 'It certainly is, Zo. It certainly is.' She felt what might have been the softest of kisses on her forehead before he relaxed his grip around her waist and drew back.

'Anyway, Zoë, if you've got the energy for an hour or two on the slopes tomorrow morning before lunch, maybe you'll allow me to try to explain why I really want you to have that little gift and why I think it's right that you take it.'

'But it isn't, Billy...'

'Come skiing with me in the morning and hear me out. If you still don't want to accept it, I promise I won't argue. All right? How does meeting in the lobby at ten tomorrow morning sound?'

'It's a date – but you won't get me to change my mind.'

'So be it, but at least we'll be able to ski together, and I'm looking forward to that. I've enjoyed being with you this week – a lot.'

–

Zoë finally made her way up to bed around one o'clock. By that time most of the other guests – including Lorna and Max – had also disappeared, and it was quietening down. As she was leaving the ballroom with Juliet, her friend reached across and nudged her in the ribs.

'Well, well, well... Do you see what I see?'

Zoë followed the direction of Juliet's gaze. There on the far side of the dance floor was none other than Grant, wrapped in a passionate embrace with some unknown woman in a silver dress. She harrumphed quietly to herself, but she was smiling as she turned back to Juliet.

'That's very kind of him. He's obviously going out of his way to prove to me that I made the right decision in telling him to take a hike.'

Back in her room, she slipped off her heels and sat down heavily on the bed, wiggling her toes in relief. She really wasn't used to wearing this sort of stuff. She stretched and leant back on her elbows, revisiting the evening in her mind. Apart from the Ron incident and his confirmation that she was in the doghouse with Damien, it had been fun, and the sensation of loneliness that had struck her at one point had been swept away by the sheer kindness and affection showered upon her by Billy – married man or not. She looked forward to skiing with him again in the morning and was determined to get him to understand why she couldn't accept the necklace.

She pulled herself to her feet and stepped out of her dress, hanging it meticulously in the wardrobe. She unclipped her little pine marten necklace and laid it on the table. As she did so, she glanced at her skiing jacket. On an impulse, she opened the side pocket and removed Billy's necklace in its packet. She unwrapped it again, opened the box and took it out, holding it up in front of her, studying the exquisite detail of the jeweller's art. She undid the clip and put the gold chain round her neck, letting it hang against her skin. It really did look wonderful and she would have so loved to keep it, but she knew she couldn't. Billy had said his new-found air of sophistication was only a veneer, and this present to a woman who wasn't his wife was an example of how naïve he still was. Regretfully she took it off again, replaced it in its box and wrapper, and returned it to her jacket pocket in readiness for the morning.

She was just coming out of the bathroom in her pyjamas when her eyes strayed to the sofa.

'Bugger! The presents.'

She had completely forgotten that she had to make her own delivery on behalf of Santa Claus to the tree in the private lounge, in readiness for what would no doubt be an early-morning assault by little Bella. She pulled on her bathrobe and slippers and packed as many of the presents as she could into a plastic bag, balancing the remainder in her arms. Then she let herself out of the door and made her way gingerly down the empty corridor towards the lounge.

It was just as she reached the empty reception desk opposite the lift that Clumsy Lumsey, her innate clumsiness, struck yet again. She felt one of the loose presents move and tried to catch it, but the next thing she knew, she had dropped the lot, some of them rolling under the glass and steel screen of the desk.

Cursing to herself, she set about picking them up. Fortunately, nothing appeared to be broken. After retrieving the presents lying in the corridor, she squeezed behind the reception desk and scrabbled around on her hands and knees, locating and collecting the others. It was while she was doing this that she heard a noise. She looked up – concealed by the screen and the miniature Christmas tree on the counter – and saw Grant's door open. Instinctively she crouched lower, peering out from among the tinsel garlands of the tree. To her surprise, she saw Erika emerge, bright red in the face. As she knelt in her hide, feeling like a hunter in the jungle, totally absorbed by the scene unfolding before her, she saw the receptionist spin round on her heels and lunge back into the room with one hand. There was the sound of a hefty slap, then the girl turned and came marching down the corridor towards the lift.

Zoë hastily ducked right down behind the counter in case she should be spotted, but Erika had other things on her mind. Quite unaware of Zoë's presence, she could clearly be heard muttering and fuming to herself as she waited for the lift to arrive. The doors closed behind her and Zoë found herself smiling. That was definitely karma. You got what you paid for in this life. She herself had never slapped Grant, but she had to admit that it had sounded good.

She reached into the half-open door of a wall cupboard, located the last two presents, which had somehow rolled in there, and stuffed then into the pocket of her bathrobe. She was just about to get to her feet again when she heard the pinging sound that announced the arrival of the lift. As she was in her pyjamas, she ducked down behind the desk once more as the doors opened, resisting the urge to giggle at the thought that this was turning into a farce. Squinting through the branches of the Christmas tree once again, she saw Lorna and Max come out into the corridor. They were wearing their coats and had evidently been for a walk outside. Lorna's room was right beside the lift, and Zoë saw her open the door and then turn towards Max with a smile.

'Thanks for a wonderful evening, Max. I thought it was going to be awful, but then you came along.'

'I had a great time, Lorna, and it's all down to you.' He hesitated. 'Maybe we could do this again some time.'

'I'd love that, Max. I really would.'

Zoë saw her reach up and pull his face down until she could kiss him, chastely, on the cheeks. He beamed at her.

'Could I call you tomorrow?'

'I'll be disappointed if you don't. Goodnight, Max, and thanks again.'

'Thank *you*, Lorna. Sleep tight.'

Zoë was smiling to herself as Max stepped back into the lift and Lorna's door closed. Maybe Lorna really had found her man. And the fact that she hadn't hauled him into her room and ravaged him had to be a very positive sign.

She was just about to get to her feet when, to her amazement, she heard the sound of yet another door. Natural curiosity made her stop and watch from her concealed position.

It was Juliet's door that had opened this time, and Zoë saw her emerge, also in her bathrobe. Presumably she too had forgotten about the presents. She smiled to herself and was about to get to her feet when she saw Juliet turn the other way and walk up the corridor, away from the lift and the lounge. Zoë hesitated, puzzled, wondering if her friend had lost her bearings. However, it soon emerged that there was nothing wrong with Juliet's sense of direction. She went up to the last room on the right, Billy's suite, and tapped softly on the door. It opened almost immediately, and Juliet disappeared inside, the door closing silently behind her.

Zoë's smile slipped from her face and the comfortable sense of amusement that had been built up by the little cameos she had observed disintegrated in a flash. She fell back to her knees, trying to come to terms with the ramifications of what she had just seen.

Juliet and Billy!

Suddenly the gold necklace made sense. Far from being naïve, Billy was revealed as the cheat he really was. Doubtless there had been other necklaces for other girls, and there would probably be more in the future. Poor Daniela. Married for barely a few months, and her husband already cheating on her. Alternatively, of course, Daniela might be happily involved with him in a *ménage à trois*. Either way, it was very distasteful. For a moment, Zoë found herself thinking about Ron and the swingers' parties Lorna had mentioned, and she shuddered at the thought. At the same time, she felt a wave of sadness at the realisation that kind, generous, friendly Billy was no different from Grant. For a moment, she felt physically sick.

And to make matters worse, the girl he had chosen for his infidelity tonight was none other than her best friend. It was so out of character for Juliet that Zoë even wondered if he had drugged her, before immediately dismissing the idea. After all, there had been no coercion involved in getting Juliet to walk up the corridor all by herself and knock on the door. She was clearly a willing partner in this adultery. This realisation only served to depress her further.

Finally collecting herself, Zoë got up and made her way along to the lounge, where she added her presents to the hefty pile already lying around the base of the tree. Santa Claus had been busy and Bella was going to have her work cut out in the morning. Realising that it was already Christmas Day – but now feeling anything but Christmassy – she headed back to her room. In spite of her tiredness, it took her a good long while before she finally dropped off to sleep.

Chapter 19

Zoë woke up late on Christmas morning, but she still felt tired after a broken night. She looked at the time and saw that it was past nine. No doubt Bella had already been up for hours, opening presents. Somehow the idea of joining in with the celebrations didn't appeal in the slightest, so she called room service and ordered breakfast in her room.

As she ate her fruit salad and drank her cappuccino, she wondered what to do next. The one thing she was sure about was that she had to get Billy to take his bribe back – because that was no doubt what it was intended to be. Maybe she was being lined up as the next girl to knock at his door. Well, if that was his plan, he had another thing coming. In the end, although she really didn't want to see him, she knew she had to speak to him alone before she could contemplate joining the other happy members of their group as they celebrated Christmas together. Consequently, after breakfast, she put on her skiing gear and went down to meet him in the lobby with a very heavy heart.

She found him waiting for her with a bright, breezy smile on his face. Christmas carols were playing on the loudspeakers, and almost everybody she saw appeared to be wearing red and white Christmas hats. There were smiles all round. But not on her face.

'Hi, Zoë, sleep well?'

'No. Did you?'

She saw surprise on his face at her tone, but she didn't want to have a scene here in the middle of the hotel lobby, surrounded by people. She went out of the door and retrieved her skis from the rack where she had left them overnight, clipping herself into the bindings without comment. As soon as she heard the double click indicating that he too had put his skis on, she scooted off ahead of him across the garden towards the ski lift.

She had every intention of getting onto a separate chair from him, but at the last moment, the lift man pushed him and a couple of other skiers on with her. Zoë at least had a solid barrier between her and Billy and was unable to speak to him, even if she had wanted to. She sat there listening to the young couple between them chatting about the presents they had given each other, while her fingers played with the necklace box in her jacket pocket.

When they reached the top, she knew what she had to do. She skied to one side and stopped. It was a freezing morning, but there wasn't a cloud in the sky. However, the same couldn't be said for the way she felt.

Billy skied up behind her and stopped alongside her.

'Is something the matter, Zoë? What's wrong?'

He sounded worried and caring. The duplicity of it sickened her.

'There's a lot wrong, Billy, and you know damn well what it is. Anyway, let's get this over with.' She reached into her pocket for the jewellery box. 'I'm surprised, and disappointed, at you. I thought you were different. It just shows how wrong you can be about people. Here. Here's your present. I don't want it. I don't want any part of it. Is that clear?'

She thrust the little box into his gloved hand and didn't give him time to reply. Turning away, she sidestepped the few metres back up to the lift and, to the surprise of the lift attendant, climbed onto an empty chair and set off back down the hill. Halfway down, she glanced over her shoulder, but Billy wasn't on the lift behind her and she felt a sense of relief. However, the thought crossed her mind that he might be skiing down to meet her at the bottom, so, when she got down there, she confused the other liftman by not getting off. She stayed on as the chair slowed and turned in a tight circle and other people queued up to climb on. She found herself sharing the lift with three young Austrian snowboarders, but she didn't mind. Anybody but Billy – or Grant.

At the top she looked about, but could see no trace of Billy. She didn't feel like skiing, so she took off her skis, stuck them in the rack and went into the restaurant. It was still quiet at this time of the morning and she found a table to herself out on the terrace and ordered a coffee. The sun was already warm and the view was delightful, but she was so wrapped up in her thoughts, she barely noticed. In fact she was so distracted that she didn't even see Juliet until she was standing right by the table.

'Hi, Zo. Where were you this morning? I thought something had happened to you?'

Zoë looked up. Juliet was smiling, but Zoë felt anything but smiley.

'I just didn't feel very sociable.' Her tone was cold and she saw Juliet look surprised.

'Can I join you?' Juliet sounded hesitant.

'It's a free country.'

'What's the matter, Zo?' Juliet sat down but kept staring at her, a look of acute concern on her face. Zoë dropped her eyes to her coffee.

'You tell me.'

'Tell you what, Zo? You're behaving very strangely. Zo, look at me. Are you all right? I'm worried about you. What's wrong?'

Zoë took a deep breath and looked up.

'You want to know what's wrong? Well, I'll tell you what's wrong, Jules. Last night I saw you going to join Billy in his suite. That's what's wrong.'

'You saw what?' Juliet looked stunned.

'I saw you in your bathrobe knocking on Billy's door, prior to spending the night with him. Or are you going to deny it?'

There was no reply for a few moments and Zoë had time to finish her coffee. When Juliet finally spoke, her voice was muted and heavy with emotion.

'Billy's suite has got two bedrooms, Zo.'

'What's that supposed to mean?'

'It means I didn't spend the night with Billy. All right?'

Seeing stirrings of comprehension on Zoë's face, Juliet continued.

'I've been waiting for the best time to tell you, Zo. You know you thought I'd been looking happier lately? Well, there's a reason for that. It's taken me years, but I've finally worked out who I am – and who I want to be with.'

'Are you telling me…?' A light bulb spluttered into life inside Zoë's head. Suddenly so much made sense. How could she have been so blind all these years? The fact that Juliet had never really had a boyfriend, her attitude to men in general, her tendency to be a bit shy, a bit of a loner, it all suddenly fell into place. Juliet was…

'Yes, Zo. I didn't spend the night with Billy. I spent the night with Danni. There, now you know. I'm gay, Zoë. I like girls. I finally worked it out at the age of thirty-two.'

Zoë looked up and saw tears in her friend's eyes. The implications of what she had just heard were still sinking in as she reached over the table and took both of Juliet's hands in hers.

'Why didn't you tell me, Jules? I'm happy for you. Very happy for you, if that's what you feel is right for you.'

'I was going to talk to you, Zo, but you've been so preoccupied with all your problems, I thought I'd wait until you'd laid your demons to rest.' Juliet glanced in the direction of the door and then, to Zoë's surprise, stood up. 'I texted Billy when I spotted you out here. I saw him down at the bottom of the lift. He's really worried about you, Zo. He's here now and I know he's got something to say to you. I'll leave you two alone. You and I can talk more later.' She hesitated for a moment before adding, 'And Zo, it's all right about me and Danni. He knows.'

He knows? Zoë's head was spinning so much by now that she barely registered Juliet's departure and the arrival of Billy.

'Zoë, can I sit down? Please?' He sounded very hesitant.

'Yes, yes, of course.' Her mind and her emotions were still in a whirl.

'I brought some schnapps. I thought we could both do with one.' He set the two shot glasses of colourless liquor on the table and pushed one across towards her.

'Here, try not to spill it.' She could hear the nervousness in his voice. 'Listen, Zoë, we need to talk.'

For a moment, Zoë remembered hearing these exact same words from Grant a year ago, and looked up in alarm. This time, she saw a smile – a nervous smile, but a smile all the same.

'I owe you an apology and an explanation, Zo.'

'*You* owe *me* an apology? Billy, *I'm* the one who should be apologising. I don't know what to say. I've behaved awfully, I've misjudged you. Talk about jumping to the wrong conclusions… I've…'

His hand reached across the table and caught hold of hers, squeezing it gently.

'Shh, Zoë, it's all right. Honestly. Just listen, will you?' Their eyes met for a moment and she saw that he was looking anything but confident and self-assured.

'Zoë, it's like this. You know I told you there was only a thin veneer over the top of the old Billy? Well, I wasn't joking.' He reached for his shot glass and took a mouthful of schnapps. 'There's something I have to tell you. It's something I've wanted to tell you for ten, eleven years, but I never had the nerve. You see, it's quite simple really – I love you, Zoë.'

'You love me?'

'Heart and soul. I have done ever since I first saw you – and in case you don't remember, it was a hot September afternoon. I was carting my bags up the stairs at number 23 and you appeared and offered to help. You were wearing a short denim skirt and a red tank top, and I thought you were the most beautiful woman in the world. I still do.'

'But Billy…' Zoë felt like a freshly landed fish, flapping about, gasping for air.

'But you had Grant, so I said nothing. Of course, I know you would never have considered me. Even I recognise what a pathetic specimen I was back then. Maybe you think I still am, even though I've tried my hardest to change.'

He swallowed the rest of his schnapps and Zoë absently pushed her own glass across the table to him.

'Here, take mine, Billy. I'm fine.' Of course, she was anything but fine. Here she was, listening to what sounded like a sincere outpouring of love from a married man – a married man whose wife had spent the night with another woman. What on earth...?

'Thanks, Zo. Anyway, back in the summer I heard that you and Grant had split up and I knew I owed it to myself to tell you how I felt about you, even if you turned me down. I know I should just have jumped on a plane and come to London to see you.' His eyes met hers for a moment and she saw him attempt to smile. 'I actually got as far as Heathrow one day last August, but I lost my nerve and climbed straight back on another plane again. Then I hit on this plan.'

'The plan being to invite us all over here for Christmas? But Billy, your wife, Daniela...?' Zoë was floundering again.

'She's not my wife, Zoë. She really *is* my personal trainer. We've been working together for almost two years now and I probably know Danni better than any other girl. She told me very early on that she preferred girls – I suppose in her line of work she often finds guys hitting on her. That was fine with me because there was... *is* only one woman in the world for me.'

He took a sip of Zoë's schnapps.

'With her help, I hatched up the plan. We'd pretend to be married. There are two bedrooms and two bathrooms in the suite, so she could be quite independent. I'd get you all over here – there's safety in numbers – and then, when I saw whether you and I were getting on well together, I'd come clean and explain. I've been trying to summon up the courage to tell you for a couple of days now, but I always chickened out at the last minute.'

'But why pretend to be married?'

'To take the pressure off – off both of us. You're a very bright girl and I knew I'd be unable to hide my attraction for you. I didn't want to frighten you off until we'd had a chance to talk. We needed to get to know each other again, to rekindle our friendship. If you thought I was just a predatory rich boy on the prowl, you wouldn't have come near me.' He managed a little smile. 'As I've been finding out over the last few years, some girls like that kind of thing, but you're far too sensible – and principled.'

The pieces were slowly starting to fall into place in Zoë's head. But he hadn't finished.

'I thought I'd ballsed the whole thing up when Grant agreed to come too. You see, I waited until you'd said yes before contacting him, making it clear that you'd be here and giving him a let-out, saying I quite understood if he preferred not to come. But then, of course, he said yes all the same. And it was blindingly obvious from the moment he arrived that he'd come with the intention of trying to get you back. All this week I've been waiting anxiously to discover that my brilliant plan had just backfired in my face, but you really have dumped him now, haven't you?'

'Grant and I are history. That's absolutely definite.' She saw a look of relief on Billy's face. 'I just don't know what to say…'

But then she remembered.

'Listen, Billy, I've got some serious explaining to do as well. I made the mistake of telling a colleague at work where I was spending Christmas, and with whom. When my editor got wind that I was coming over here to see you, he did his best to bully me into writing an article for the magazine about you, the *reclusive* billionaire. I've been like a cat on a hot tin roof all week, wondering how and when I should speak to you about it, but I didn't have the nerve. I almost told you up at the castle that marvellous morning, but like you, I chickened out. Anyway, just so you know, I sent him an email two days ago, telling him I wasn't going to do it, and that's why he sent that bloody photographer last night.'

'Lorna told me all about her mistake in inviting him to the ball. It wasn't her fault and I told her so. How was she to know he had a hidden agenda? I didn't realise you were involved, though.'

'I wasn't. In fact, if *she* hadn't called security, *I* would have done. Apparently I'm likely to lose my job as a result of all this, but I knew I couldn't betray your trust.'

'I wouldn't worry about that. It doesn't sound like a very nice company to work for anyway.' He swallowed the last of the schnapps and stood up so suddenly, he startled her, and she overturned her coffee cup – fortunately already empty. He reached into his pocket and retrieved the box with the gold necklace and laid it on the table.

'I hope you *will* accept my little gift now. I'd really like you to. Anyway, I've said what I've been waiting years to say. If you feel like thinking about it, I'd be very, very happy. Take your time. Take as long as you like. I'll wait… another ten years if I have to.'

Before she could make any kind of response, he turned, hurried back into the cafe and disappeared from sight. Zoë sat blankly, desperately trying to process everything she had heard that morning. She felt tears stinging in the corners of her eyes, but she didn't really know why.

Chapter 20

When she got back to the hotel, Zoë went straight to Juliet's room and knocked on the door, desperate to make things right between the two of them once again. The first thing she did was to give Juliet a warm hug and beg her pardon.

'I'm so, so sorry for thinking the worst of you, Jules. I think it was because I'd just met up with that sleazeball photographer. For a moment my brain was running along the same disgusting lines as his. Please, please forgive me. You're my very best friend and I feel simply awful.'

'Nothing to forgive, Zo. I should have told you months ago that I'd finally come out, but I wasn't sure how you'd take it. You were already so miserable, I didn't want to make things worse for you.'

'You're so sweet. You could have told me. I'd just have said what I'm saying now. I'm really, really happy for you. You look and sound so much more cheerful than you've done over the past few years, and that's great.'

'Can I ask, Zo? Did Billy tell you about his plan?' Zoë nodded and Juliet looked relieved. 'Danni told me last night, but she said it was a big secret. Now he's told you, so that's fine.' She caught Zoë's eye. 'Him not being married has got to be just about the best possible news you could have, isn't it?'

'I suppose so.'

'You suppose so? You do realise he's hopelessly in love with you. Danni says you're all he ever talks about.'

'Yes, that's what he told me, too.'

'You don't sound terribly excited. Surely you feel the same way about him, don't you? I've seen the way you've been looking at him.'

'The way I've been looking at him? Have I really been making eyes at him?' She remembered what Grant had said the previous night. 'I suppose I must have been – even Grant commented.'

'See? So, what are you going to do about it?'

'What can I do? We're going home in two days' time.'

'You can do a lot in two days, Zo.'

–

Christmas lunch was a real traditional feast – but not an Austrian one. The chef produced a full English Christmas lunch for them, complete with turkey, stuffing, chipolata sausages, sprouts, gravy and all the trimmings. There were even English crackers containing silly hats and even sillier jokes. Zoë had to admit that the food was a damn sight better than the lunch she had prepared the previous year, although, to be honest, she had barely touched her food back then as her whole world disintegrated around her. Now she was able to eat, but the confusion reigning in her head was once again overwhelming – although far less demoralising.

Predictably, the meal was accompanied by the finest wines and champagne. Billy sat at the head of the table, with Daniela at his right hand. Zoë took a seat in the middle, with Juliet on one side of her and Bella on the other. Throughout the meal the little girl chattered incessantly about all the presents she had received – and the new bike Santa had delivered to her home address, to await her return. Zoë listened with half an ear as she ate her lunch and the others read out the corny jokes from the crackers, all the while turning over in her head everything Billy and Juliet had said to her. Juliet was right, of course. She had been thinking a lot about Billy, but the knowledge that he was married had very firmly dampened down any romantic notions. Now that she suddenly found him no longer forbidden fruit, she had a lot of rethinking to do. From time to time she snatched glances at him and did her best to process the results.

There was no getting away from the fact that he had morphed into a good-looking, sophisticated man, and of course he was still as kind as ever. Even more appealing was the fact that remnants of his shy former self still lay, barely concealed, beneath a thin covering of hard-won self-confidence. There had definitely been moments – like when they had been skiing together, or when he had held her close as they danced last night – when she had imagined him in a romantic light, but there was a problem. Now that he had declared his love, and she knew him to be unattached, an elephant had just come lumbering, uninvited, into the room.

He was a billionaire.

How could she, Zoë Lumsley, possibly fit in with his lifestyle? He divided his time between here and what was no doubt an amazingly expensive house in California. He rubbed shoulders with film stars and cabinet ministers and dealt in millions of dollars. She thought back to her own rented flat, her scruffy old car and her underwear that badly needed replacing. There was an abyss between the two of them, in many ways just as wide as there had been at number 23. Back there, he had been the timid little nerd and she the popular girl sharing a bed with the captain of rugby. Now the roles were reversed, but the abyss between them remained.

Her thoughts were interrupted by the arrival of a monster Christmas pudding, flambéed and burning with a blue flame. According to Billy, this had been sent over specially for the occasion, along with Devonshire clotted cream and real custard. There were oohs and ahs of appreciation on all sides, but to Zoë, this extravagance further emphasised the gap between her lifestyle and Billy's.

After lunch, they all went through to the lounge – led by the excited little girl and the Labrador – to open the rest of the presents around the tree. In fact, just about the first present to be opened was for Arnie from Daniela. It was a squeaky toy convincingly shaped to look like a shoe. As the dog grabbed it with delight, Daniela raised her hands helplessly.

'I know it's an admission of defeat, but he's already ruined two pairs of perfectly good shoes.'

As it turned out, the dog received a number of other chewable toys, and for the rest of the afternoon, all that could be heard from him was a regular chorus of squeaks.

Zoë's teddy bear for Bella earned her a hug and a kiss, and the snow globes of Bad Bergstein, decorative candles, mugs and cuddly toys were greeted with appreciation and amusement by the others. She had bought something for everybody, including Georg and Marcel, and even found something for Erika – whose face-slapping episode last night had endeared her to Zoë once more. Billy was delighted with the framed photo and they all took turns to study it, mostly remarking upon how young and skinny they all looked in it. After serious reflection, she had even bought something for Grant – a packet of chocolate Mozartkugeln. As she whispered to Juliet, the 'balls to you' message seemed appropriate.

She received a number of presents, ranging from chocolates to perfume, and even socks. Billy's presents were the same for everybody – fine-looking pens individually engraved with each person's name and, simply, *Bad Bergstein*.

When all the presents had been opened, they settled down to a lazy afternoon together. Zoë slipped back to her room and phoned her mum and dad. She must have sounded happy, because both her mother and her father commented – with discernible surprise in their voices. Zoë reflected that this past year must have been tough on them as well. She told them all about the hotel, the skiing, the gala ball and the traditional Christmas lunch, as well as her final expulsion of Grant from her life, but she didn't mention Billy specifically, because she really didn't know what to say. 'And by the way, Mum, a billionaire says he's in love with me' would have necessitated most of the afternoon to explain. She resolved to talk it through with them once she got back home. Maybe by then she would have managed to sort things out in her own mind.

Back in the lounge, Bella had opened a new set of coloured pens, and they took turns at drawing and writing on Martin's plaster cast. Then, after a while, at the little girl's insistence, they were all cajoled into playing party games, culminating with hide-and-seek. Their individual bedrooms were declared out of bounds, so there were limited places on the top floor for them to hide. When Bella screwed up her eyes and started to count up to twenty, Zoë saw people duck for cover behind sofas and armchairs and under tables in the lounge, so she went out into the corridor. Seeing Grant disappear into the dining room, she decided to try elsewhere and went on along the corridor. Remembering the cupboard she had spotted when in her hiding place the previous night, she slipped behind the reception desk and found the narrow door set in the wall. It was still unlocked, and inside she could see stationery, towels and toiletries. She was just squeezing through the low doorway when she heard a whisper from the shadows inside and jumped.

'Mind out for the mop and bucket on the right. The mop's still wet. Come and join me in the middle of the toilet paper. Over to your left.'

'Is that you, Billy?'

'It's me all right. I used a bit of local knowledge. How come *you* thought of hiding here?'

Zoë squeezed in alongside him and pulled the door closed behind her.

'It's a long story. Let's just say I noticed it last night. I'll tell you all about it sometime.'

There wasn't lot of room in the cupboard and she found herself pressed against him so close she could feel his heart beating – and it was beating fast. As she crouched there in the pitch dark, feeling her own heart rate begin to rise, her mind turned over and over, and gradually some sort of revelation began to dawn.

The fact was that everybody in their group had been pretending to be something they weren't.

Lorna had arrived pretending to be her same happy, hedonistic self of old, while all the time, deep inside, she was hankering for a different life, where she could make a fresh start and settle down. Seeing her turn her back on Ron the photographer and, more importantly, initiate what might hopefully develop into a genuine relationship with Big Max had cheered Zoë no end. Things were looking good for Lorna.

Imogen had been so desperate to give the impression of opulence, she had resorted to trying to trick the others with her borrowed clothes. Whether it was the advice she had received from Zoë, or the shock of fearing something had happened to her husband, she now appeared to have accepted him for what he was – a good man who would make her happy, irrespective of whether he would ever become as rich as Crocsus. As the days had gone by, she and Fergus had emerged as a normal, loving couple.

Mandy, beneath the outward show of happy families, had been nursing a feeling of guilt that threatened to overwhelm her. After finally finding the strength and the courage to tell her husband what had happened, their relationship appeared, once more, to be the stable, loving one it had always been.

Dear Juliet had been fighting against her natural instincts all her life, and it was only so very recently that she had finally found happiness with the admission to herself that she now knew her true orientation. Giving up the pretence had brought new meaning into her life – and maybe a special someone in the shape of Daniela. Zoë was especially pleased for her that things were working themselves out.

And then there was Grant. In his case, he had been trying to convince her that he had transformed into a reformed character, no longer predatory and shallow. Instead, he had once more revealed himself in his true colours – with the morals of a tomcat – and Zoë felt sure he was a lost cause. But at least he was no longer *her* lost cause.

Finally, of course, this lovely, kind man who was sandwiched between her and a pile of toilet rolls had revealed that he too had been putting on an act. This wonderful Christmas holiday had been an elaborate charade to bring him close to the girl he claimed to have loved for over ten years. It was somehow so very sweet that this apparently sophisticated, successful man with a cosmopolitan lifestyle had been so insecure he had had to resort to such tactics. Her heart went out to him.

But the fact of the matter, she now realised, was that she too had been pretending – though in her case to herself as much as to other people. It gradually became clearer and clearer in her mind. She had managed to convince herself that after the Grant debacle she wasn't interested in anything but her career. It had taken a sweet little girl and a kind and generous friend this week to make her realise that she really did want to settle down and find happiness with somebody. What now emerged like a blinding light in spite of the darkened confines of this broom cupboard was that there was no doubt in her mind that the man crushed up against her in the middle of a heap of toilet paper was that somebody. The fact that he was amazingly rich was something with which she would have to learn to come to terms, but it didn't alter the way she felt about him.

Suddenly it all became clear in her head and she felt an overpowering urge to kiss him. She raised a hand and reached forward very gently with her fingers, making contact almost immediately with his cheek. She let her hand slide round to the back of his head and then slowly pulled him towards her.

'Billy, there's something I've got to do. I hope you don't mind.'

She kissed him.

It wasn't a passionate kiss – just a gentle touch of lips upon lips – but the effect it had upon her was overwhelming. As her lips rested against his, she felt that same sense of belonging and happiness she had felt in his arms on the dance floor the previous night. It was a warm, comforting sensation that swept away the hurt and the heartache of the previous twelve months, and she felt tears spring once more to the corners of her eyes. Her precarious composure totally deserted her and a few seconds later, in spite of her best efforts, she was crying her eyes out.

She felt his arms reach out and cradle her, pulling her tightly towards him and rocking her like a little baby. As she sobbed into his cheek, she heard his voice – hardly more than a breath.

'It's all right now, Zoë. It's all right.'

They stayed like that for probably a couple of minutes, until she gradually began to regain control of her emotions. Finally she raised her head and reached out again, catching hold of his cheeks and leaning forward so that her eyes were only a couple of inches from his. By now she had grown accustomed to the dark, and a narrow ray of light coming through the crack of the door reflected in his eyes. Without blinking, she kissed him again, just to be sure. The sensation was the same as before and she felt a smile forming on her face.

She shifted slightly on the toilet rolls and was about to speak when a sudden agonising stab of cramp gripped her thigh. She squeaked in pain and kicked her leg out straight ahead, making contact with something. Seconds later, she felt a cold, damp sensation on her foot. However, the good news was that her sudden movement had nipped the cramp in the bud and she was able to relax again. Doing her best to ignore the wet mop on her foot, she looked back up at Billy.

'That was the bucket.'

'I heard.' She could hear the barely suppressed mirth in his voice. 'Some things never change, do they, Zo?'

'*You've* changed, Billy.'

'Not in the way I feel about you, Zoë.' His voice was suddenly serious again.

Wet foot or no wet foot, she felt herself smiling at him. He pulled her closer, and this time he kissed her and she abandoned herself in his arms. It was a good long while before she felt like talking again. Finally she drew back and rested her cheek against his, whispering into his ear.

'Billy, what you said to me up there on the terrace this morning, I never said thank you. That was the sweetest thing anybody's ever said to me and I'll never forget a single word of it.'

'So do you think there's hope for me?' His voice was still hesitant and her heart went out to him.

'Oh yes.'

He kissed her again, and she knew it felt right.

Billy and Zoë won the hide-and-seek competition hands down. Bella took so long to find their hiding place that Zoë was beginning to feel more twinges of cramp by the time the door was pulled open and excited squeaks from the little girl and similar noises from the Labrador's rubber shoe alerted them to the fact that it was time to stop what they were doing. She climbed out, groaning as she straightened up, doing her best to ignore the ominous squelching sounds from her wet foot, and rewarded Bella with a smile. Behind her, Billy emerged with a broad grin on his face that lasted for the rest of the afternoon.

At four o'clock, they had a visitor. To everyone's delight – particularly Lorna's – it was the big American. Shouts of 'Hi, Max!' went up across the room, and Lorna made sure she timed her greeting to coincide with his head brushing against the mistletoe.

He came armed with chocolates, cakes and a gorgeous stuffed toy in the shape of a black Labrador for Bella. It was hard to decide who liked it better, Bella or the dog, but Zoë got the feeling the toy's days would be numbered if the little girl let Arnie get hold of it.

Marcel arrived shortly afterwards with a Christmas cake, Stollen, and tea for those who wanted it, along with ice cold champagne for those who preferred something stronger. Zoë, now having changed her shoes, had been lolling on the sofa with a silly expression on her face ever since emerging from the broom cupboard. She needed no persuading to accept a glass of champagne from Billy, who sat down beside her. As they sipped their wine, they chatted about random things like snow, skiing and Christmas. If she had been asked later to recall what they had talked about, she would have found it near impossible. All the time, the only thing in her mind was the realisation that something had fundamentally changed in her life. She now knew that she was no longer alone.

A bit later on, Billy swallowed the last of his champagne and stood up.

'And now Arnie's got a rendezvous with his favourite tree. He and I had better pop out for a walk.'

At the sound of the magic W word, Arnie appeared at his master's feet, tail wagging.

Zoë immediately leapt to her feet to accompany him. True to form, she forgot she still had half a glass of champagne in her hand, and the next thing she knew, she had tipped it all over the Labrador once more. Arnie jumped back in surprise and then subjected her to the sort of disapproving look Damien reserved for her more outrageous articles. She blushed and dropped to her knees, stroking his ears with one hand while scrabbling for a tissue with the other. As she did so, a huge cheer went up around the room, accompanied by catcalls.

'Nice one, Zo!'

'Clumsy Lumsey strikes again!'

As she mopped the worst of the wine off the dog's back, she glanced up at Billy apologetically.

'Just as soon as I've dried your dog off, I'd love to come for a walk with the two of you.'

Outside, the sun had just dropped below the rim of the mountains, but the sky was a light purple colour and she could still make out the onion-shaped cupola on the church and the roofs of the old town in the distance. Zoë caught hold of Billy's left arm in both hands and rested her head against his shoulder as they strolled along the winding path beneath the trees. A few minutes later, the Christmas lights in the trees blinked into life and she saw a few tiny snowflakes beginning to fall, sparkling in the light, adding a magical feel to the evening. Neither of them spoke, but it didn't matter. In spite of the cold, she was warmed by that same glow of happiness and belonging. It just felt right.

As they reached a clump of silver birch trees, Billy slowed and stopped. Without a word, he drew her to him, slipped one arm around her back, the other around her neck, and pulled her tightly against him. As her eyes gently closed, she felt his lips upon hers as he kissed her – this time with real passion – and she responded.

It was some time before he spoke.

'I didn't ask. Can I take it that this means you *will* accept my little gift?'

Zoë patted her pocket and checked that the box was still there, then took a step back and unzipped her jacket. Reaching behind her neck, she unclipped the little silver chain bearing the pine marten and held it out towards Billy.

'I'm very, very definitely going to accept your gift and I promise I'll cherish it forever. In return, here's a little memento of the wonderful times you and I have spent together. It's only a little token, but I wonder if you'd accept it as a gift from me to you. I don't expect you to wear it all the time, but maybe you'd like to keep it.'

She saw his eyes sparkle in the Christmas lights.

'For the rest of my life.'

He opened his jacket and leant forward so she could clip the silver chain around his neck. Then she removed the box from her pocket and opened it. She slid the gold necklace onto the palm of her hand and held it out towards him.

'Would you mind?'

After he had fastened the necklace around her neck, he took her in his arms and kissed her again. She felt her knees go weak, and if his strong arms hadn't been around her, she would probably have ended up in a snowdrift. That same feeling of happiness spread all over her. She felt protected and she felt loved. Finally coming up for air, she looked up into his eyes.

'Why me, Billy?'

'There's never been anybody else, Zoë. I knew it from the very first moment I saw you, but I can't explain it. That's just the way it is. Over the past years I've been in and out of a number of relationships, but none of them has lasted any length of time. Nobody else has ever matched up to you – and nobody ever will.'

'Oh Billy…'

Suddenly she felt almost like crying all over again. Instead, she hugged him tightly and kissed him again.

It was a good deal later when they were finally roused by the Labrador jumping up against their legs, reminding them of his presence. They both knelt down to pet the dog and, as they stood up again, Billy caught hold of her hands in his.

'Zoë, I was wondering something. Do you have any plans for after Christmas?'

She shook her head. 'No, nothing special. I don't go back to work until the third of January – assuming I've still got a job to go back to. Why do you ask?'

'I wondered if you might consider staying on. Daniela told me she's going over to spend a few days in London with Juliet when she and the others go home the day after tomorrow, so there'll just be me and Arnie left.'

Zoë didn't need time to reflect.

'I'd love that, Billy. I really would.'

'And my suite's got two bedrooms, so you wouldn't need to feel…'

For a moment, the old, insecure Billy reappeared in his tone. Zoë reached up and linked her fingers behind his head, pulling his face down towards hers.

'One bedroom's going to be fine, Billy… just fine.'

Acknowledgements

With many thanks to Michael Bhaskar and all the team at Canclo for all their support, help and encouragement.